T of South Shropshire

by M. Allbutt, J. Moseley, C. Rayner & P. Toghill

Edited by

J. T. Greensmith

3rd Edition

©THE GEOLOGISTS'
ASSOCIATION
2002

CONTENTS

i

PREFACE

The previous Guide to Shropshire, written by the late Professor W.F.Whittard, was published to commemorate the Centenary of the Geologists' Association in 1958. This was later revised by W.T.Dean in 1968. Much, besides a radical change in Guide format, has happened in the intervening years, not least in matters as basic as the availability of geological maps. Thus in 1958 South Shropshire (which we take as that part of Shropshire south and west of the valley of the River Severn) was covered only as part of the Shrewsbury 1-inch sheet first published in 1932. (A new edition on a 1:50000 scale was published in 1978 as sheet number 152). Then in 1967 completion of a 6-inch geological survey gave a 1-inch Church Stretton sheet which was followed, in 1967, by a metric 1:50000 version (sheet 166) together with four innovative 1:25000 Classic Area maps for Church Stretton, Craven Arms, Much Wenlock and Ludlow-Leintwardine. Further 1:25000 scale maps then followed for the Shelve Inlier and Telford. Finally with 1:50000 sheets for Montgomery (165) in 1994 and Ludlow (181)in 2001 coverage is now almost complete - a small area in the extreme southwest between Teme and Clun valleys awaits a Knighton sheet (214) expected *circa* 2005.

It is therefore opportune to publish a new guide with itineraries grounded in a well understood and documented stratigraphy that spans all periods from Precambrian through to Triassic and covers lithologies from volcanic tuffs and lavas through fossiliferous marine and fluviatile sediments to aeolian sandstones. Moreover, the area has continued to attract academic study and research. For example the relationship between Precambrian volcanics (Uriconian) and sediments (Longmyndian) is now better understood, type sections for much of Silurian received global recognition in the 1980's, similar sections generally continue to be accepted for parts of the Cambrian and Ordovician and historical geology, as determined by plate tectonics, is established to a satisfactory degree. Appropriately in 2001 Ludlow was the venue for the 50th anniversary field meeting of the Ludlow Research Group the eminent members of which have made major contributions to worldwide research in the Silurian.

South Shropshire has traditionally attracted student groups from schools, colleges and universities keen to use its sites for training and project works. A number of the older classic localities and sequences are now incorporated into Geological Trails, specifically the Ercall Quarries of The Wrekin, the Onny Valley Trail, the Mortimer Forest Trail and, most recently, the Teme Bank Trail at Ludlow, all with descriptive booklets or leaflets. If these trails are viewed as introductory then this guide can be considered as a logical follow-up both extending their content and encouraging wider exploration.

Since 1958 it can certainly be claimed that access to sites and viewpoints in rural areas is much improved with all footpaths and bridle ways marked on OS maps and large areas of previously closed Forestry Commission lands now giving a freedom to roam. Less helpful is the almost total decline of rural bus services and an increase in traffic on the main A-roads to a level which effectively debars their use by the pedestrian. This can cause some logistical difficulties in the design of a walking itinerary since it has to be assumed that the guide user will arrive at the start by vehicle and wish to return to the same place to recover it. Whilst a circular itinerary is therefore desirable, occasionally this could involve a return, which merely reverses a stratigraphic sequence already examined. In such a case it is hoped the reader will appreciate the reasons for possible "options" and suggestions about "transport arrangements". Above all please share with the authors the thrill of finding that the older classic areas of Shropshire still have the capacity to inspire and the newly presented areas to surprise and intrigue.

Acknowledgements

The four authors, all members of the Shropshire Geological Society, wish to thank that body for its support and generous donation towards individual costs of preparation, also Hereford & Worcester RIGS Group for a similar contribution, Dr. J. D. Lawson for his valuable comments on the Mortimer itinerary and Susan Beale who, as Secretary of the SGS, initiated and guided the early steps of this project. Also to be thanked are landowners and/or their tenants, mentioned in the text, who have generously agreed to allow access to their properties with a minimum of restrictions.

The bulk of the printing costs for the Guide were generously defrayed by a grant from the Curry Fund of the Geologists' Association supported by a grant from English Nature through the auspices of Jonathan Larwood.

Most of the maps were re-drawn by Colin Stuart. Figure 1, the general geological map of the area, appears by permission of the British Geological Survey (IPR/25-14C BGS.© NERC. All rights reserved).

LIST OF FIGURES

THE GEOLOGICAL HISTORY OF SHROPSHIRE

The geology of Shropshire, and in particular the south of the county where all these walks are situated, is remarkably varied, and includes sedimentary rocks and fossils from the majority of the recognised periods of geological time (Figures 1 and 2). A wealth of literature has been published about the area including numerous maps and guides by the British Geological Survey. Good summaries of all the literature can be found in Cocks (1989) and Toghill (1990, 2000). The area was often close to plate boundaries in the past and this has resulted in a complex geological history, which is reflected in the variety of faults and folds that are found. Plate movements also account for a number of volcanic sequences and episodes of intrusive igneous activity, particularly in the older rocks.

The late Precambrian eon, 700 to 544 million years ago

The oldest rocks in Shropshire are the little-known Rushton Schists which occupy a small area west of The Wrekin and probably form a Monian type basement to the whole of the area. The metamorphism has been dated at 667 million years ago, and the rocks are quartz-epidote-garnet schists indicating metamorphism of a pelitic sequence. The Primrose Hill Gneisses and Schists, which occupy a small area at the southwest end of The Wrekin ridge, are probably altered Uriconian Volcanics injected with granophyric material.

The oldest rocks occupying any considerable area are the Uriconian Volcanics and Longmyndian sediments. These are found along and between the Church Stretton and Pontesford - Linley Faults, and are dated at between 566 and 560 million years old. Both these fault systems were probably initiated in the late Precambrian but continued to affect sedimentation in Shropshire right up into the Tertiary period.

The Uriconian Volcanics probably represent a cordilleran–style, subaerial volcanic arc situation with a calc-alkaline sequence of lavas and ashes formed close to the edge of the Gondwana continent when that area was around 60 degrees south of the equator. The area was probably made up of volcanic islands , with an adjacent marginal basin. The volcanics show a strong within-plate component in their geochemistry and may have erupted through continental crust.

The early part of the Longmyndian sequence, which includes some sediments with volcaniclastic debris, was probably deposited in a fore-arc basin adjacent to the volcanic arc, at the same time as the lavas and ashes were being erupted from the nearby volcanoes. The coarse grained later Longmyndian sediments represent erosion of the Uriconian arc after cessation of the volcanic activity.

The Uriconian Volcanics include at least 1500m of rhyolitic lavas and ash flows, as well as andesitic and basaltic lavas. These form the well-known hills of The Wrekin, Caer Caradoc, The Lawley and Wart Hill along the Church Stretton Fault System, and Earl's Hill at the northern end of the Pontesford

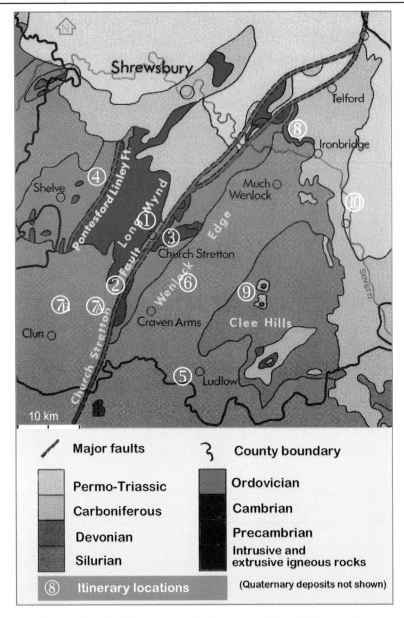

Figure 1. Outline geological map of South Shropshire (after Toghill, 1990) and itinerary locations. Based on the United Kingdom (Solid), 1:625000, 3rd Edition (1979) map by permission of the British Geological Survey, IPR/25-14C.

PERIOD/SYSTEM	EPOCH/SERIES	FORMATIONS
QUATERNARY	Holocene	River Terraces, Alluvium, etc
	Pleistocene	Glacial Drift
TERTIARY		
CRETACEOUS		Sediments Absent in Shropshire
JURASSIC		
		Present in North and East Shropshire
TRIASSIC		Present in North and East Shropshire
		Wildmoor Sandstone
		Kidderminster Conglomerate
PERMIAN		Bridgnorth Sandstone
		Alberbury and Enville Breccias
CARBONIFEROUS	Westphalian	Upper Coal Measures
		(Clee Hill Dolerite intruded)
		Variscan folding and faulting
		Middle Coal Measures
		Lower Coal Measures
	Namurian	Cornbrook Sandstone Formation
	Dinantian	Carboniferous Limestone
		Little Wenlock Basalt
		Lydebrook Sandstone
DEVONIAN	Upper	Farlow Sandstone
	(Old Red Sandstone)	Clee Formation
		Late Caledonian folding, Acadian
		St Maughans Formation
	Lower	Bishop Frome (Psammosteus)
		Limestone Member at base

PERIOD/SYSTEM	EPOCH/SERIES	(West of CSF)	(East of CSF)
SILURIAN	Pridoli	Clun Forest Formation	Raglan Mudstone Formation
			Temeside Shale Formation
			Downton Castle Formation
			(Ludlow Bone Bed at base)
	Ludlow	Cefn Einion Formation	Whitcliffe Formation
		Knucklas Castle Formation	Lower & Upper Leintwardine Formation
		Bailey Hill Formation	Upper Bringewood Formation (Aymestry Limestone)
		Oakley Mynd Formation	Lower Bringewood Formation Lower, Middle & Upper Elton Form.
	Wenlock	Aston Mudstone Formation (Edgton Limestone Member)	Much Wenlock Limestone Form. (Wenlock Limestone Member) (Tickwood Beds Member)
		Bromleys Mill Shales Formation	Coalbrookdale Formation (Buildwas Member) (Ape Dale Member)
	Llandovery	Purple Shales Formation Pentamerus Sandstone Formation	Purple Shales Formation Pentamerus Sandstone Formation
		Kenley Grit	

CSF = Church Stretton Fault, PLF = Pontesford-Linley Fault

Figure 2. Stratigraphic sequence in South Shropshire.

Figure 2 continued

PERIOD/SYSTEM	EPOCH/SERIES	FORMATIONS	
ORDOVICIAN	Ashgill	No sediments in South Shropshire	
		Intrusion of Corndon & Breidden Dolerites, and Maddocks Hill camptonite	
		Shelveian folding and faulting, early Caledonian	
		West of PLF	East of PLF
	Caradoc	Absent	Onny Shales
			Acton Scott Group
			Cheney Longville Flags
			alternata Limestone
			Chatwall Sandstone & Flags
		Whittery Shale & Volcanics	
		Hagley Shale & Volcanic Formation	Harnage Shales Formation
		Aldress Shale Formation	
		Spywood Sandstone	Hoar Edge Grit
	Llandeilo	Rorrington Shale and Meadowtown Formation	Absent
	Llanvirn	Betton Shale Formation	Absent
		Weston Flags Formation	
		Hope Shale Formation including Stapeley Volcanic & Hyssington Volcanic Members	
	Arenig	Mytton Flags Formation	Absent
		Stiperstones Quartzite	
	Tremadoc	Habberley Shale	Shineton Shale F.
CAMBRIAN	Merioneth	Dolgelley Beds	
	St David's	Upper Comley Sandstone	
	Caerfai	Lower Comley Limestone	
		Lower Comley Sandstone	
		Wrekin Quartzite	
PRECAMBRIAN		*Cadomian folding and faulting*	
		Wentnor Group (Western Longmyndian)	
		Bridges & Bayston Oakswood Formations	
	Longmynd Supergroup	Stretton Group (Eastern Longmyndian)	
		Portway Formation	
		Lightspout Formation	
		Synalds Formation	
		Burway Formation	
		Stretton Shale Formation	
	Uriconian Volcanics	Rhyolitic, Andesitic & Basaltic, lavas & ashes.	
		Acid Intrusions	
		Primrose Hill Gneisses and Schists (? Altered Uriconian)	
	Rushton Schists		

PLF = Pontesford-Linley Fault   CSF = Church Stretton Fault

Linley Fault. At Overley Hill, just west of The Wrekin, rhyolites have been dated at 566 million years old. The Uriconian Volcanics are intruded by a number of basic dykes, and the acid boss-like granophyre on the Ercall has been dated at 560 million years old.

The Longmyndian Supergroup is formed of about 7000m of mainly shallow water sedimentary rocks which are subdivided into two major lithological groups, the mainly fine grained Stretton Group (or Eastern Longmyndian), followed by the coarse grained Wentnor Group (or Western Longmyndian).

The Stretton Group comprises 3500m of marine shales and mudstones, with turbidites at the base, but also includes some volcaniclastic material. Deltaic sandstones appear later indicating a shallowing of the water. Volcanic ashes at certain horizons indicate the proximity of the volcanic arc producing the Uriconian Volcanics at the same time. A tuff near the top of the Stretton Group has been dated at 556 million years old (Compston, Wright & Toghill, 2002). Bentonitic volcanic ashes are abundant in the lower part of the sequence east of the Church Stretton Fault System and one has been dated at 567 million years old.

The overlying Wentnor Group probably covered a wider geographical area following cessation of volcanic activity and infilling of the fore-arc basin with fine grained early Longmyndian sediments. The group consists of 3500m of coarse red, and purple-brown sandstones, with thick conglomerate horizons indicating alluvial flood plains and braided rivers. This modern interpretation (Pauley, 1986) of the Longmyndian does not include the classic unconformities of earlier writers at the base of the Longmyndian, or at the base of the Wentnor Group. Pauley also considers the early Longmyndian to be coeval with the Uriconian Volcanics.

At the end of the Precambrian, the Cadomian orogeny deformed the Uriconian Volcanics and Longmyndian into an overturned syncline, and this was probably a transpressive event with a good deal of tear faulting along the Church Stretton and Pontesford - Linley Faults, and within the Precambrian sequences. Basic dykes were intruded during the later stages of the deformation and fracture cleavage formed, particularly within the finer sediments, but no true metamorphic cleavage was produced.

The Cambrian period, 544 to 510 million years ago

A long period of erosion followed the Cadomian orogeny at the end of Precambrian times and this may well have continued into the early part of the Cambrian period, before a marine transgression deposited the Wrekin Quartzite over the whole of the area. The overlying, relatively thin, Cambrian sequence contains the famous Comley Limestones, found near Church Stretton, which include the *Callavia* trilobite fauna of Lower Cambrian age. Cambrian rocks are restricted to the Church Stretton area and the area around The Wrekin.

The Ordovician period, 510 to 440 million years ago

A deepening of the sea in early Ordovician times produced the Shineton Shales, which were deposited over the whole of the county. It was at this time that Avalonia split away from Gondwanaland and the associated rifting produced uplift and a regression of the sea away from Shropshire towards the Welsh Basin in the west. By the Arenig epoch the shore line between the Avalonian continent and the Welsh Basin lay along the Pontesford - Linley Fault. This led to a remarkable feature of the Ordovician rocks in Shropshire whereby an almost complete sequence was laid down west of the Pontesford - Linley Fault in the Shelve area and only a thin sequence east of the fault, around Church Stretton, represented by deposits laid down during the later Ordovician Caradoc transgression.

In the Shelve area to the west of the Pontesford-Linley Fault, the Shineton Shales of Tremadoc age are followed by a complete Arenig, Llanvirn and Llandeilo sequence of sandstones, shales, and volcanic lavas and ashes, the last produced in an island arc or marginal basin setting, off the coast of Avalonia. To the east, an arid landmass bordered the sea, but this was transgressed at the start of the Caradoc epoch and a marine shallow water sequence of sandstones and thin limestones was laid down to the east of the Church Stretton Fault, the type Caradoc area. This important marine transgression was probably caused by an increase in global plate tectonic activity. The increase in size of mid-ocean ridges, and the subsequent increase in volcanic activity might have caused a worldwide rise in sea-level leading to a spreading of the sea over continental shelves.

During the succeeding Ashgill epoch a major glaciation was centred over North Africa and this caused a worldwide fall in sea-level, and the sea over Shropshire regressed westwards into the Welsh Basin. Thus there are no Ashgill sediments in Shropshire apart from in the far northwest of the county. The sea-level also fell because of a plate tectonic event, the Shelveian event. Avalonia had by now reached 35 degrees south of the equator and at this time collided with the Baltic micro-continent (Baltica). This collision caused folding of the Ordovician rocks of Shropshire, as seen in the steep dips of rocks adjacent to the Church Stretton Fault in the type Caradoc area and in the folding in the Shelve area, plus movements along the Pontesford - Linley and Church Stretton Faults. The Shelveian event also brought about a number of other major and minor faults within the Precambrian and Lower Palaeozoic sequences, such as the Stiperstones Fault and the Sharpstones Thrust. Lateral movements along the Pontesford - Linley Fault may have been as much as 40km displacing the Shelve area from its original position adjacent to the Builth -Llandrindod inlier of Ordovician rocks. The extensive mineralisation which affects Ordovician rocks in the Shelve area, and also the northern Longmyndian outcrop, is probably of Devonian or early Carboniferous age.

The Silurian period, 439 to 409 million years ago

The Silurian period in Shropshire started with a major marine transgression during the Llandovery epoch this producing a conspicuous basal unconformity. The sea spread slowly from west to east over an irregular landscape with the Shelve and Longmynd areas forming islands. Old Silurian beach lines with sea stacks can be mapped around the southern end of the Longmynd. Early Silurian brachiopod communities indicate increasing depths of water and allow the position of the shore line to be mapped with a good deal of accuracy over the Midland Platform.

During the Llandovery epoch the sequence was the same over the whole of the county, but from the Wenlock epoch onwards the sequence is very different either side of the Church Stretton Fault System. East of the fault the Wenlock and Ludlow epochs are made up of alternations of shales and limestones. The Much Wenlock Limestone, formed at 25 degrees south of the palaeo-equator, is famous for its coral reefs which are very similar to patch reefs forming today in the Caribbean. West of the Church Stretton Fault the sequence passes into the deeper water of the Welsh Basin and limestones of the shelf areas are replaced by mudstones carrying only thin calcareous horizons. However, by the time of the youngest Silurian Pridoli epoch shallow waters again generally prevailed over most of Shropshire. The shallow water sediments indicate the progressive rise of Shropshire above sea-level during the early part of the Caledonian Orogeny.

The Devonian period, 409 to 363 million years ago

During the early Devonian the Caledonian Orogeny reached its climax over northwest Britain. In Shropshire the Silurian rocks were gently folded to produce the low dips of the Wenlock beds and the classic folding of the Ludlow anticline. New faults were initiated and further movement occured along the older fault lines. The Devonian sequence in Shropshire is represented by the Old Red Sandstone, which occupies Corvedale and the lower slopes of the Clee Hills. The sediments are all continental types formed on lowland plains between the Caledonian Highlands to the northwest and the Rheic Ocean to the south, which covered Devon and Cornwall.

The Carboniferous period, 363 to 290 million years ago

By the end of the Devonian period the Old Red Sandstone continent had been eroded almost down to sea-level and a shallow warm subtropical sea spread over southern Britain including Shropshire to form the Carboniferous Limestone. St Georges Land, or as it is better known today the Wales-Brabant Massif, was situated across Shropshire so that the Carboniferous Limestone sequence in the south of the county on Titterstone Clee Hill was formed as part of the South-West Province. However, that found at Llanymynech Hill in the northwest of the county, and also the outcrops at Lilleshall and Little Wenlock belong to the Northern Province. On Titterstone Clee there was probably continuous deposition through Old Red Sandstone into early Carboniferous times, whereas in the northern outcrops there is a major unconformity at the base of the Carboniferous, which rests on rocks ranging in age from Cambrian to Silurian.

Later in the Carboniferous period rivers flowing into the warm shallow sea started to produce large areas of deltaic sands and muds, which now form the well-known Millstone Grit succession of the Pennines. Southern Britain now lay astride the equator and as time progressed the deltas and swamps started to support tropical rain forest growth in a very humid climate. By Coal Measures time these lush rain forests and freshwater swamps were widespread, and were repeatedly affected by invasions of the sea. Ultimately the thick layers of decaying vegetation were converted by presssure and heat into productive coal seams.

Millstone Grit type sediments are not well developed in Shropshire but are found on Titterstone Clee Hill and also in the Oswestry area. The overlying Coal Measures form the highest parts of the Clee Hills where they are intruded by a dolerite sill, locally called the dhustone.   The Coal Measures of the Coalbrookdale Coalfield east of The Wrekin and around Ironbridge were exploit-ed in the 18th and 19th centuries, when this area cradled the Industrial Revolution using local coal, iron ore and limestone.

A number of unconformities occur within the Carboniferous sequence in Shropshire, indicating early phases of the Variscan Orogeny. A particularly important one occurs at the base of the Upper Coal Measures, locally known in the Ironbridge area as the Symon Fault. Elsewhere, the Upper Coal Measures overstep all the older Carboniferous rocks and rest on Ordovician and Longmyndian rocks in the Shelve and northern Longmynd areas. Here, thin but important coal seams were used for smelting lead ore from the local mines in the Ordovician outcrop.

The late Carboniferous-early Permian Variscan Orogeny caused uplift, faulting and small-scale folding in the Shropshire area. Many of the Shropshire coalfields are affected by quite complex faulting. On Titterstone Clee Hill, a faulted syncline, which also effects the local dolerite sill, has dips up to 20 degrees in places. By the end of the orogeny Shropshire, along with most of Britain, lay within the arid hinterland of Alfred Wegener's Pangaea at a latitude of about 25 degrees north of the equator.

The Permian and Triassic periods, 290 to 208 million years ago

During this long interval of time a Sahara-like desert area covered Shropshire with large areas of sand dunes separated by arid highland areas. Later on rivers flowing through the desert areas laid down thick sands and gravels and playa lakes evaporated to leave thick salt deposits. Permian and Triassic sedimentation probably affected the whole of Shropshire, but outcrops are found today only in the north and east of the county where they pass into the large areas of the Cheshire and Midland Plains.

The Jurassic and Cretaceous periods, 208 to 65 million years ago

At the very end of the Triassic the very arid landscape was transgressed by shallow waters of the Tethys Ocean, which spread from the east. Early Jurassic clays and limestones, as part of the Liassic sequence, are found as outliers in north Shropshire but there are no later Jurassic or Cretaceous sediments. However, it is likely that post-Liassic marine sediments from these periods were laid down but were later eroded away during the Tertiary period. During the Jurassic and Cretaceous Shropshire moved steadily north to about 45 degrees north of the equator.

The Tertiary period, 65 to 2 million years ago

Shropshire, along with other parts of Britain, experienced uplift and erosion during the Tertiary due to the Alpine Orogeny. The climate during early Tertiary times was warm and humid with erosion progressively stripping off the cover of Jurassic and Cretaceous sediments, and much of the Permian and Triassic from South Shropshire. The characteristic landscape of the South Shropshire hills would have emerged during the later Tertiary with the initiation of the present river systems, although many of these would suffer diversion during the Quaternary ice ages. It is probable that many of the major faults in north Shropshire affecting the Permian, Triassic and Jurassic rocks were initiated during the Alpine movements and renewed movement occurred along many of the older fault lines, including the Church Stretton Fault. Vertical movements along that fault downfaulted Silurian rocks into the Church Stretton Valley.

The Quaternary period, 2 million years ago to the present

There is no evidence in Shropshire of what was happening during the early parts of the Quaternary period when there were least 17 cold phases that affected Britain as recorded in the North Sea. There is also little evidence in the county of events during the Anglian or Wolstonian glacial phases, which affected Britain between around 300,000 and 150,000 years ago. However, the last glacial phase, the Devensian, which started 115,000 years ago and finished 10,000 years ago, had marked effects on the geomorphological development of the county.

Evidence suggests that the early Devensian was a very dry cold period with little snowfall and hardly any glaciation anywhere in Britain. A marked deterioration in climate around 70,000 years ago was followed by severe glaciation over most of northern and western Shropshire between 23,000 and 15,000 years ago, with the southern limit of the Irish Sea ice in the Church Stretton Valley. Although ice in Scotland probably exceeded 2000m in thickness and over 1000m occurred in Wales, it appears that the actual thickness of ice in Shropshire during the Devensian was never more than 400m.

The Geological History of Shropshire

Shropshire was the meeting ground of Welsh ice from the west and Irish Sea ice from the north. The highest summits of the South Shropshire hills stood above the ice and were subject to severe freeze-thaw conditions, which produced the tors and screes of the Stiperstones and the screes of the northern slopes of Titterstone Clee Hill. Although no valleys in Shropshire were over deepened by a valley glacier, resulting melt waters often eroded valleys to new lower levels. This was certainly the case in the Church Stretton Valley where the Irish Sea ice reached its southern limit. Melt-waters took the level of the main valley down to a new lower level and this meant that streams cutting down on the eastern side of the Longmynd were rejuvenated and cut particularly steep young valleys, the well-known batches.

A number of rivers, including the Teme, Severn and Onny, had their courses diverted by the presence of ice, which blocked their original drainage directions. Perhaps the best-known diversion of all is that of the River Severn, which used to flow out to the Dee estuary north of the Cheshire Plain, but whose direction was changed by the cutting of the Ironbridge Gorge during the melting of the Devensian ice sheets. The classic interpretation is that the gorge was cut by water from a large proglacial lake at the retreating ice front over-flowing the Wenlock Limestone escarpment, but it is more likely that the gorge was cut by melt-waters under pressure from the ice sheet when it was locked against the escarpment.

With the melting of the ice sheets, starting at around 15,000 years ago, a thick blanket of glacial sands and gravel, and boulder clays, was left behind over many parts of Shropshire, as well as a number of terminal moraines. Many of the upland areas are covered with head and solifluxion deposits. As the tundra climate eased woolly mammoths migrated up from the south of England and an almost complete adult mammoth skeleton, dated at 12,700 years old, was discovered in 1986 near Condover, along with bones from three juveniles.

By the start of the Holocene epoch, 10,000 years ago, the Shropshire landscape looked not dissimilar to that of today, and since then rivers have continued to cut their channels deeper, laid down modern alluvium and created river terraces reflecting their previous higher positions.

ITINERARY 1

THE LONGMYND AREA

Preface

The purpose of this itinerary is to examine representative sections in the late Precambrian sedimentary sequence that forms the Longmyndian Supergroup. A fairly demanding walk of 8km is necessary to examine the lower part of the Longmyndian succession in the valley called Ashes Hollow. Localities in the upper part are widely scattered so transport is essential.

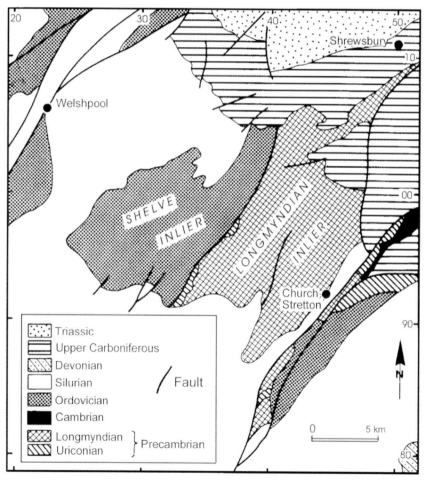

Figure 3. Longmynd and Shelve Inlier.

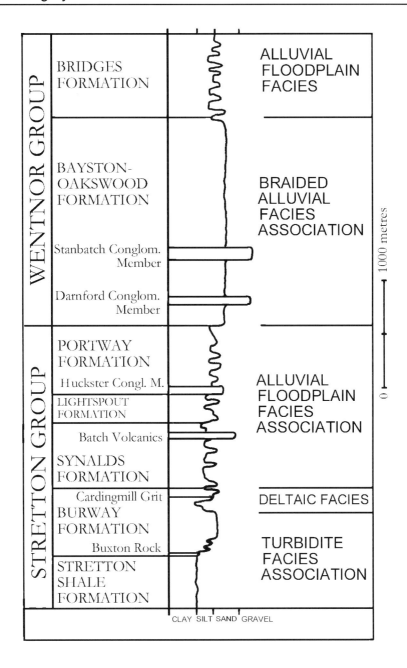

Figure 4. Longmynd Supergroup.

The Longmyndian Supergroup crops out over an area of 65 km² that extends from the A49 Shrewsbury - Ludlow road in the east almost to the Stiperstones ridge in the west, and from 10km south of Shrewsbury in the north to the A489 Craven Arms - Newtown road in the south (Figure 3). Part of this area is formed of a very distinctive plateau called the Longmynd that rises to 516m above sea-level, and is cut by several deep, steep-sided valleys that offer excellent exposures. Much of the Longmynd is owned by the National Trust but there is ready public access, sometimes via permissive and public footpaths across farmland.

Hammering is discouraged but at most localities there is sufficient loose rock material for representative samples to be collected. The following maps are recommended for use with this itinerary: OS Explorer Sheet 217 (The Longmynd and Wenlock Edge) 1:25000 and the British Geological Survey 1:25000 series The Shelve Ordovician Inlier and Church Stretton (SO 49).

Introduction

Pauley (1990) has interpreted the late Precambrian Longmyndian Supergroup as a prograding turbidite to alluvial flood plain sequence (Figure 4). He suggested that the Ragleth Tuffs should, on the basis of lithological similarity, be included in the Longmyndian Supergroup rather than the underlying Uriconian Volcanic Group. The accurate stratigraphy of the Longmyndian Supergroup is partly established upon the identification of narrow, lithologically distinctive marker horizons, such as the Buxton Rock, Cardingmill Grit, Batch Volcanics and various conglomerates, which can be traced across the Longmynd area.

On the basis of minor associated folding and way-up criteria, such as sedimentary structures and bedding - slaty cleavage relationships, the Longmyndian Supergroup is believed to be folded into an isoclinal syncline trending north-northeast to south-southwest and plunging 8°/192°(Pauley, 1986). The Pontesford and Church Stretton Faults, to the west and east respectively define the margins of the Longmyndian block. Strike slip movements have dominated these faults.

Stretton Group

Ashes Hollow

Limited parking is available in Little Stretton, which can be approached south-wards from Church Stretton on the minor road that parallels the A49 and Shrewsbury - Cardiff railway line. Alternatively, turn off the A49 onto this minor road 0.5km south (SO 442911) of Little Stretton. In Little Stretton turn in a westerly direction down a narrow minor road next to the Ragleth Inn (SO 443918). After 150m a T-junction is reached adjacent to a stream (Figure 5). Park tight to the stream to allow access in all directions for farm vehicles. The walk of 8km can include a tough climb to the top of the Longmynd for views, and then a steep descent. This part of the excursion is not for the faint-hearted and by retracing the

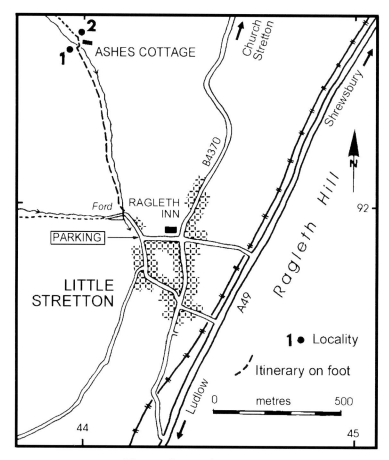

Figure 5. Little Stretton.

route down valley the steep climb can be avoided (Figures 8 & 9). With appropriate planning, a circular route up Ashes Hollow then north to the head of Cardingmill Valley and south eastwards down this valley into Church Stretton will provide a stimulating day's geology and exercise.

On foot, follow the road and stream northwards for 120m. Cross the ford and stile, and keep to the clear footpath northwards across a field often used for camping, and then into a long, narrow field. Again the footpath is clearly defined and, with the stream to your right, cross another stile.

Thinly bedded grey shales of the Stretton Shale Formation are exposed next to the footbridge (locality 1). Pauley (1990) suggests that these shales and the overlying mudstones and shales of the Burway Formation represent a phase of turbidite deposition. There is evidence of some small-scale fold structures, but these are not

Figure 6. View looking north from the head-covered slopes of the Longmynd, above Church Stretton. In the foreground is the steeply incised Townbrook Hollow. Across the verdant Stretton Valley, mantled with glacial drift and overlying Silurian sediments, are the Uriconian volcanic hills of Caer Caradoc, The Lawley and The Wrekin aligned along the upthrown side of the Church Stretton Fault.

as intensely developed here as in some exposures around Church Stretton. These small-scale structures reflect the incompetent nature of this formation and its response to the folding that affects the Longmyndian Supergroup and movements on the adjacent Church Stretton Fault System. Strata exposed in Ashes Hollow form part of the eastern limb of the inferred isoclinal syncline and mainly dip steeply to the west and northwest.

Cross the footbridge over the stream (SO 439926) next to the uninhabited Ashes Cottage and turn left into the Hollow. Ashes Hollow has been selected as a GCR site by the JNCC (Carney *et al.* 2000) because of the almost continuous exposure from the top of the Stretton Shale Formation to the Synalds Formation.

In a small disused quarry (SO 439926, locality 2) on the northeast side of the stream, 60m north of the footbridge, Stretton Shales give way to the thickly bedded Buxton Rock, which is recognised in thin-section as a silicified, rhyolitic dust tuff (Greig *et al.* 1968, Pauley 1990, Wilson 2000). This is a thin (2 - 8m), distinctive stratigraphic unit that crops out at several other localities, and has been used as a stratigraphic marker horizon. The following sequence dips at 63°/276°:

Dust tuff masses, very irregular with shale partings, evidence of brecciation	270 cm
Shale	0 - 4 cm
Dust tuff, in places brecciated	5 - 18 cm
Shale, with very thin lenses of dust tuff	4 - 15 cm
Dust tuff, brecciated	67 cm
Dust tuff, nodular	38 cm
Shale	15 cm
Breccia	124 cm
Dust tuff, no shale partings, individual beds 4 - 35cm	142 cm
Shale	6 cm
Dust tuff	25 cm
Dust tuff	26 cm
Shale	5 cm
Dust tuff	13 cm

The lower beds of grey, silicified, splintery rhyolitic dust tuff, display undulating wavy surfaces with an amplitude of 10cm and a wavelength of 55cm. These give way to beds that include pillow-like masses. The beds with their ovoid masses are separated by thin shale horizons (0 - 15cm) suggesting quiet, non-volcanic deposition

Figure 7. Exposures in Ashes Hollow of the turbidite facies in the Longmyndian Burway Formation (near locality 4). Ashes Hollow is one of the several 'batches' on the southeast flank of the Longmynd and shows a vee-shaped cross-section with overlapping spurs indicating stream rejuvenation during the melting stage of the last glaciation.

between pulses of volcanic input. Included is one pillow-like mass of breccia, with angular fragments (1 - 4cm); it is unclear whether this rock is a lapilli tuff, or a result of brecciation, caused when hot pyroclastic material (possibly a flow) suddenly came into contact with cold sea water. Some of the upper irregular beds show at their base brecciation with fragments of volcanic rock exhibiting either fine laminations or flow banding, the latter implying a rhyolitic or pyroclastic flow origin. Tectonic features need to be taken into account when interpreting this volcanic sequence. The thickly bedded silicified volcanics have behaved in a rigid, competent way to various phases of earth movements. Quartz-filled tension gashes are developed at right angles to bedding in some layers, due to tensile stresses during folding and uplift. Some brecciation of the volcanics may be tectonic, rather than volcanic, while the very thin shales have deformed and flowed between the thicker, more rigid volcanics. There is a passage from the Buxton Rock into the overlying Burway Formation, which, like the Stretton Shales, is interpreted by Pauley (1990) and Wilson (2000) as a sequence of turbidites. Sandstones, siltstones and mudstones of this formation are clearly exposed in the hollow adjacent to the footpath for the next 700m (locality 3) and are described in detail by Wilson (2000). The sequence is well bedded, sometimes finely laminated and there is fine graded bedding with the contrast between sand, silt and clay grade. With the exception of the development of a small anticlinal fold (Figure 8) this formation dips steeply to the west and northwest. Slaty cleavage is weakly developed, but is slightly steeper than bedding, indicating correct way up. Three hundred and ten metres beyond the Buxton Rock outcrop and just before a tributary valley leading north-northeastwards an unstable scree slope has developed (SO 436929). Crags high on the valley side have been deeply weathered, frost shattering probably dominating, and much loose poorly sorted material has resulted. Thin vegetation and poor soil cover contribute to a potential for slope failure.

Leave the footpath next to the stream before the Hollow narrows to a small gorge and follow the narrow sheep track (with care!) up the eastern side of the Hollow to reach Ashes Hollow Quarry (locality 4, SO 434930). Here again there is excellent exposure of vertical mudstones and sandstones of the Burway Formation. Evidence of the problematic pit and ring structures once called 'Arenicolites' (Salter, 1856, 1857) and interpreted as annelid burrows can be found in spoil at the incut just beyond the north face of the quarry. These have since been described as possible air-heave structures (Greig, et al. 1968), while current thinking has returned to an organic origin of uncertain biological affinity (Cope, 2000). 'Arenicolites' are preserved in thin mudstones with fine, pale to darker greyish-green, internal laminations.

Forty metres beyond the quarry there is the first of several outcrops of the Cardingmill Grit next to and above the path (locality 5). The Cardingmill Grit, a thickly bedded greywacke sandstone, is more resistant than the underlying mudstones and overlying shales. It is a distinctive medium- to coarse-grained rock that is generally dark, but with much quartz veining and like the Buxton Rock can be used as a stratigraphic marker horizon. Pauley (1990) interprets the Cardingmill Grit as a deltaic sand succeeding the turbidites of the Burway Formation as conditions

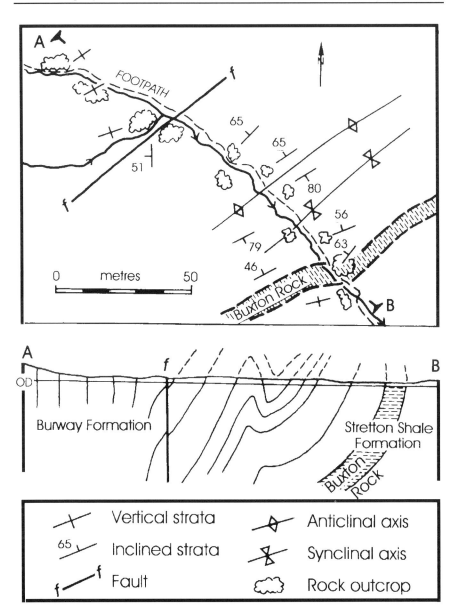

Figure 8. Folding developed in the Burway Formation.

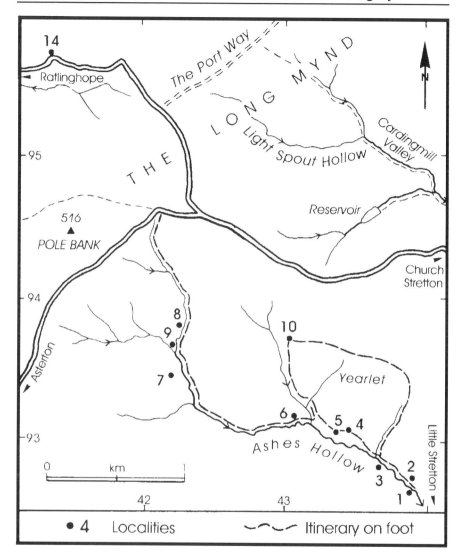

Figure 9. Locality map for Ashes Hollow and part of the Longmynd.

became more shallow. Sandstones interbedded with the highest mudstones indicate a passage into a deltaic environment.

Avoid the narrow sheep path dropping steeply downhill to the left and continue northwards on the high footpath for 270m, and immediately after crossing a very minor stream turn left and return to the Ashes Hollow stream.

A shorter alternative route from here is described below.

Continue up Ashes Hollow from the confluence with the tributary stream at SO 431931. Care should be taken on the narrow footpath along the steep valley side. Reversal of the regional dip direction at SO 431931, locality 6 where strata dips at 46°/097°, indicates local folding with a similar axial trend to the main Longmyndian isoclinal syncline. The valley floor soon widens and levels out, and the more gently sloping hillside to the north displays scattered exposures of the mainly reddish-purple shales of the Synalds Formation, with the pyroclastic horizons of the Batch Volcanics. Continue for about 500m northwards up the Hollow to the confluence with a small tributary stream that is marked by a marshy area (SO 422936, Figure 9).

High on the steep west valley side is a distinctive outcrop called Narnell's Rock (SO 422934, locality 7), an exposure of the conglomeratic sandstone known as the Huckster Conglomerate Member. Although displaced by a small fault this stratigraphic marker can be examined at more accessible exposures about 500m to the north (SO 422939, locality 8).

Dolerite dykes showing associated baked margins are exposed close to the stream confluence (locality 9). The dolerites are a very dark black-blue colour when fresh, but weather to produce a whitish or orange surface easily recognised in the field. Several exposures in this area indicate proximity to the north-south trending Ashes Hollow Fault and some smaller faults. The Huckster Conglomerate Member is displaced by c. 200m, there is a very small displacement on a dolerite dyke, minor faults are seen at Narnell's Rock and tension gashes in competent sandstone beds in this area may be related to faulting. Continuing to the top of the Hollow look out for several more outcrops of dolerite intruding grey siltstones and sandstones of the Lightspout Formation. On the Port Way, the minor road along the top of the Longmynd, there are excellent views westwards to the Stiperstones and eastwards to the Church Stretton valley and the Uriconian hills of Caer Caradoc and The Lawley.

From here there are various options, as outlined above, for either returning down Ashes Hollow, or extending this itinerary to include Cardingmill Valley.

Alternative return route to Little Stretton

From the Cardingmill Grit exposure (locality 5) continue as directed and instead of turning left after crossing a minor stream continue up what is an unnamed tributary valley onto a clearly defined footpath. Progress up valley parallel to and on the east side of the tributary stream to Ashes Hollow.

Thin purple and red shales of the Synalds Formation succeed the Cardingmill Grit. These shales, of which there are many small exposures next to the footpath, sometimes form a semi-continuous outcrop. They dip steeply to the northwest, usually exhibiting a slaty cleavage that is steeper than bedding indicating correct way up. Continue up the tributary valley and 500m above the confluence with Ashes Hollow turn right away from the stream upslope to a low ridge (SO 430936, locality 10) of purple shales with a more resistant, more massive, whitish weathering rock. This is

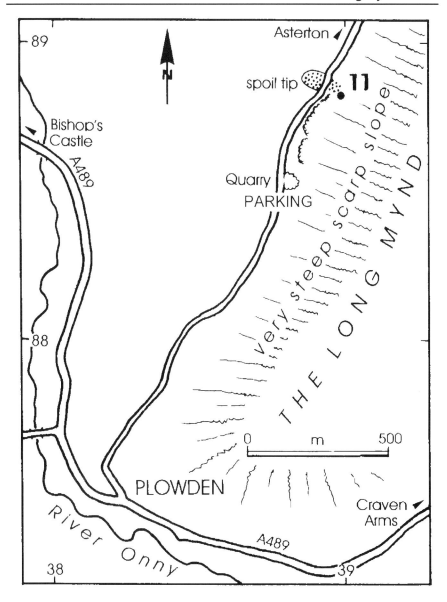

Figure 10. Locality map for southwest Longmynd.

a reworked fine- to coarse-grained tuff with some lapilli that is typical of the pyroclastic horizons that form the Batch Volcanics the useful stratigraphic marker. Pink feldspars and volcanic grains, purple shale clasts and dark chloritic lapilli are identifiable in hand-specimen. Slaty cleavage is again steeper than bedding and chloritic and felspathic lapilli are clearly flattened in the plane of the cleavage. Some of the vertical joints, at right angles to the volcanics-shale contact, display small displacements of up to 60cm producing very minor faults. Those who do not enjoy a steep climb are advised to return down Ashes Hollow to the vehicles. The route is not clearly defined here but proceed upslope, swing eastwards (to the right) towards the top of the minor tributary valley described above, or towards the ridge named Yearlet on the OS map. The climb levels out on the top of the Longmynd, and the route south-eastwards (no real footpath, but easy walking) parallels Ashes Hollow to the right, or southwest. Assuming a clear day there are superb views across and northeast-wards down the Church Stretton Valley and parallel ridge of hills defining the line of the Church Stretton Fault System. The steep sided Caer Caradoc and Lawley Hills, and others, along the ridge are upfaulted blocks or horsts of the Precambrian Uriconian Volcanic Group. The fault pattern is more complicated than simply two parallel faults. Notice the change of slope where Uriconian Volcanics form steep gorse and bracken covered hillside in comparison to lower more gentle pasture and small wooded ridges underlain by Silurian shales and limestones. This line marks the position of the F 1 component of the Church Stretton Fault System and this brings Uriconian Volcanics against the downfaulted Silurian strata which floor the valley. From this excellent vantage point turn south towards Ashes Hollow and carefully descend the very steep sided valley that comes out in the Hollow near the scree described earlier. Return to the vehicles. The sites to be examined next lie on the west side of the Longmynd. The shortest route to these is by taking the steep Burway Hill road westwards out of Church Stretton. However, this narrow road rises steeply above Cardingmill Valley, with limited passing places and a very severe drop to the right. It is not recommended for the faint-hearted, and this road is not maintained in winter. To avoid the Burway Hill, from Little Stretton continue south for 1.2km on the A49 and turn right onto the minor road signposted for Bishop's Castle. After 4km turn right onto the A489 Craven Arms - Newtown road and continue for 2.5km. Just before Plowden turn right down a very minor road that appears quite suddenly and initially almost parallels the A489. After 100m this minor road to Asterton bears sharp right so that you are now heading north. Continue for 1km, the western scarp of the Longmynd will appear to your right, and park at the roadside. There are grass verges and a very small quarry (SO 388885) providing adequate space for several cars or a minibus. The steep, quite spectacular western Longmynd scarp is fault controlled. Longmyndian rocks are upfaulted to the east. To the west Silurian strata, overlain by superficial deposits, occupy the lower undulating ground, where there is evidence of drumlin formation.

Walk northwards along the road and to the east are large crags of purple sandstones, mudstones and shales of the Portway Formation (Figure 10). Look for evidence of faulting and mineralization. There is some brecciation and slickenside development, almost certainly due to the immediate proximity of the Longmynd Scarp Fault. The fault breccias often contain some thin tabular barite and there is sparse haematisation. Continue to the small bend in the road, 325m beyond the small quarry. To the west, the hummocky made- ground is the site of small spoil tips. Turn right and climb the slope covered with shale fragments and bare of vegetation. Some shale fragments are stained with green malachite. Ten metres above the road is a small, but most significant, outcrop (SO 390888, locality 11) displaying Middle Llandovery breccio-conglomerate with a very slight westerly depositional dip resting unconformably on grey Longmyndian shales dipping 65°/270°. This is an excellent example of a breccio-conglomerate and contains rounded pebbles of quartz and quartzite and angular shale fragments. The very mature fraction of pebbles, on the basis of lithological similarity, is believed to have been derived from a Longmyndian conglomerate nearby, possibly the Huckster Conglomerate. Erosion of the underlying Portway Shales will have provided the shale clasts. The sandy matrix contains some brachiopods and corals indicating a Middle Llandovery age. This rock represents a basal shoreline deposit laid down by the transgressive Middle Llandovery sea that spread from west to east. The Longmynd and Stiperstones ridge probably formed islands in this shallow sea.

Malachite staining is common on the shales and the overgrown spoil tips are the likely result of small trials. Sparse malachite deposits are known elsewhere on the west side of the Longmynd, but all those are thought to have remained uneconomic to exploit. There is a good view northwestwards to the Stiperstones ridge with the resistant crags of Ordovician sandstones standing out very clearly. Return to the vehicles and continue northwards for 3km.

Wentnor Group

Turn left at Asterton towards Wentnor and 250m beyond this small village turn right (northwards) towards Ratlinghope and Shrewsbury. After 4km turn right into the hamlet of Bridges. Roadside parking is very limited, but there is a small car park for the Three Horseshoes Inn (SO 393964). Purple siltstones of the Bridges Group crop out in a small disused quarry (SO 393965, locality 12) next to the Wentnor - Shrewsbury road, and in the bank on the north side of the minor road between the old Youth Hostel and small bridge (SO 396964, locality 13). This area is thought to lie within the core zone of the Longmyndian isoclinal syncline. All the purple siltstones are steeply tilted, mainly westwards, but with sufficient variation in dip to suggest the possibility of minor tight folds. Way-up criteria are important in any structural analysis of these rocks. This remains difficult to assess in the field because the sediments are very fine-grained.

Continue eastwards over the small bridge and follow the road sharply left after 200m. Proceed cautiously on this narrow road and after 0.5km turn right onto the quite steep minor road that leads eventually to the top of the Longmynd. Purple sandstones of the Bayston-Oakswood Formation are exposed at the roadside between the cattle grid and T-junction, but parking here is very restricted. Two hundred metres beyond (east of) the cattle grid there is an obvious (but unsigned) car parking area (SO 413956) safely off the road to the left. Walk up the road to the roadside conglomerate outcrop (S0415956, locality 14) taking care not to obstruct traffic. Several conglomerate horizons occur in the Western Longmyndian. This is the

Stanbatch Conglomerate Member and consists of 105m of conglomerates, sandstones and pebbly sandstones. These are interpreted as braided floodplain deposits (Pauley, 1990). It is interesting to identify the pebbles. Many are composed of quartz or quartzite, but some are rhyolites and other acidic igneous rocks, and some varieties of schist have been recognised.The sandstones are coarse to very coarse-grained and quite immature; pink feldspars, glassy quartz grains and a range of lithic fragments are discernable.

Return to the vehicles. To rejoin major roads for return journeys go back to the T-junction just beyond the Three Horseshoes Inn and turn right to go northwards to Shrewsbury and left to eventually link up with the A489 around the south end of the Longmynd. For those unconcerned by the steep, unfenced Burway Road continue eastwards across the Longmynd and down into Church Stretton.

ITINERARY 2

WART HILL AND HOPESAY COMMON

Preface

Wart Hill is a small, late Precambrian inlier 3.5km west of Craven Arms. The aim of this excursion is to examine the diversity, structure and stratigraphy of the Precambrian Uriconian Volcanic Group that forms Wart Hill, and the relationship as a fault-bounded inlier within the Church Stretton Fault System to the slightly younger Precambrian sandstones of the Longmyndian Supergroup. To reach Wart Hill turn off the A49 Shrewsbury to Ludlow road at the north end of Craven Arms onto the minor road heading westwards and signposted for Edgton (Figure 11). This road crosses a railway line and continues uphill in a general westerly direction. Soon after the road levels out, there is a bend, a short downhill section and Wart Hill comes into view on the right (north) side of the road. The hill has a thick cover of mature conifers. There is restricted parking on the roadside for a small number of vehicles by the access gate to Wart Hill. Please do not block this entrance as forestry work is sometimes in progress. Although the route is short, part of one track is almost permanently waterlogged. There is a steep climb to the top of Wart Hill by way of a permissive footpath and a difficult descent to a stream section. Access to Wart Hill is by kind permission of Major Minton-Beddoes acting for the tenants Forest Enterprise.

Wart Hill and Hopesay Common are ideal for a half-day excursion with a maximum walking distance of 3km. Shops, inns, etc. are available at Craven Arms and 11km to the northwest of Wart Hill at Bishop's Castle. Rock outcrops are very small so hammering is not advisable. Please enjoy and respect this attractive part of south Shropshire.

Recommended maps: OS Explorer Sheet 217 (The Longmynd and Wenlock Edge) and 216 (Welshpool and Montgomery) 1:25000: Geological Sheet 8048 Craven Arms 1:25000.

Introduction

The Precambrian rocks of south Shropshire are divided into the Uriconian Volcanic Group, a suite of calc-alkaline volcanics composed mainly of andesites, rhyolites and dacites with some pyroclastics and dolerites, and the slightly later Longmyndian Supergroup. The Longmyndian is a thick (*c.* 6000m) turbidite to flood plain sequence with distinctive pyroclastic and conglomeratic horizons.

The Church Stretton Fault System, an important structural element of the Welsh Borderland, can be traced from north Staffordshire, where it is known as the Red Rock Fault, southwestwards through Shropshire and into South Wales (Carmarthenshire), where it aligns with the Careg Cennon Disturbance. The Church Stretton Fault has a Caledonoid trend and along it there has been some folding and

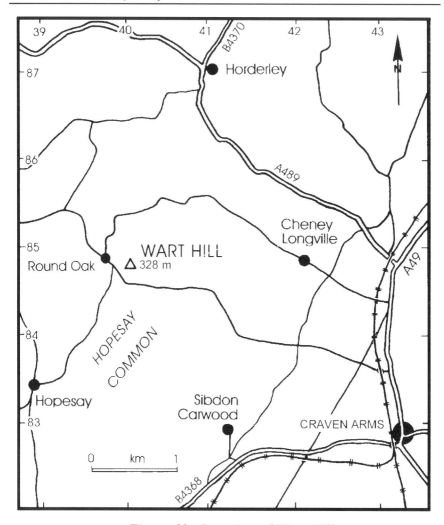

Figure 11. Location of Wart Hill.

thrusting. Most fault movements are described as transpressional, with a tear component exceeding vertical displacement. There has been frequent reactivation and a complex structural history has developed through the late Precambrian and Lower Palaeozoic.

Uriconian Volcanic Group

Park at the access point to Wart Hill adjacent to, but not blocking, the padlocked gate, by the minor road from Craven Arms. Follow the permissive footpath

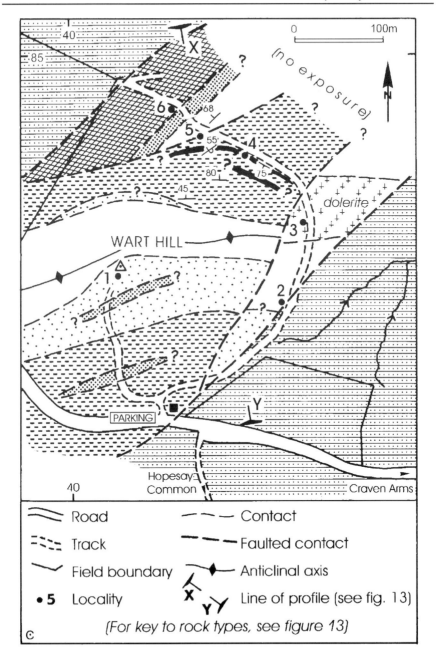

Figure 12. Locality and geological map of Wart Hill.

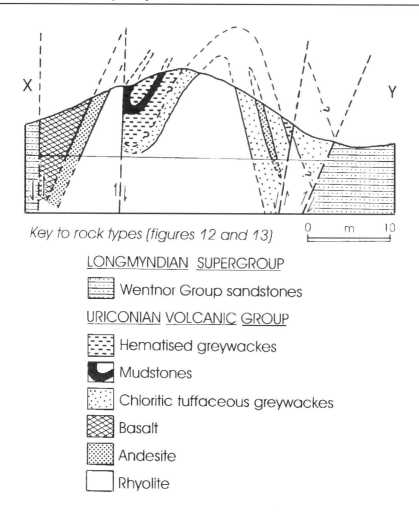

Key to rock types (figures 12 and 13)

0   m   10

LONGMYNDIAN SUPERGROUP

Wentnor Group sandstones

URICONIAN VOLCANIC GROUP

Hematised greywackes

Mudstones

Chloritic tuffaceous greywackes

Basalt

Andesite

Rhyolite

Figure 13. Geological cross-section through Wart Hill.

sign to the summit of Wart Hill. Immediately south of the Trig. Point (SO 401847) are very small exposures (locality 1) of tuffaceous, conglomeratic greywackes. (Unless otherwise stated all rocks described in this itinerary are part of the Uriconian Volcanic Group.) These clastic rocks are very poorly sorted. Angular pink feldspars and pale volcanic fragments stand out from the generally dark chloritic matrix. The Geological Survey Memoir (Greig *et al.*, 1968) reports that these greywackes, and some interbedded andesites, dip steeply to the southeast. The rocks form part of the southern limb of the Wart Hill anticline the axis of which trends 070° (Figures 12 and 13) and is located slightly north of the Trig. Point.

Further evidence for this fold is described below.

Although partly obscured by conifers there are excellent views, which can also be appreciated from some vantage points on the approach road to Wart Hill and from Hopesay Common (see below). To the north the Church Stretton Valley, a distinctive depression between Caer Caradoc (upfaulted Uriconian) to the east and The Longmynd to the west, marks the continuation northwards of the Church Stretton Fault System. Eastwards and striking away to the northeast is the Wenlock Edge showing classic dip and scarp topography. The Silurian strata that form the edges and vales are the Wenlock and Aymestry Limestones which alternate with Ludlow and Wenlock Shales. The more resistant limestones form forested scarps, while softer shales underlie the pasture land of the vales. Rolling countryside to the south is underlain by Silurian strata, and to the west the more rugged terrain of the south part of the Shelve Inlier consists of Ordovician volcanics, shales and intrusives.

Return from the summit and continue on a track that extends around the east and north sides of Wart Hill. Initially this track is parallel to an adjacent field boundary. It is worthwhile trying to identify any loose rock fragments on the track. Usually these are composed of fractured, fine-grained, pink to grey rhyolite or, less commonly, dark greywacke and breccia. Do not turn right onto the path that leads eastwards but continue to where the track may be extremely waterlogged. This marks the location of a component of the Church Stretton Fault System. In 1980 widening and clearing of this forestry track revealed a fault zone (locality 2, SO 402847) with coarse-grained conglomeratic purple sandstones of the Precambrian Longmyndian Supergroup to the east. The fault zone is 61cm wide, dips steeply to the northwest and consists of pale grey, saturated gritty gouge. Excavation of the saturated soil that forms the partially overgrown bank on the northwest side of the track will reveal the fault. This, however, is a wet and very muddy task.

Continue on the track, which for a short distance remains very wet, and after 80 metres a deeply weathered outcrop of dolerite (locality 3, SO 403848) can be examined. This is just before the track turns sharply to the northwest. No fresh dolerite is exposed, and the extent of this intrusion is unknown.

Beyond the turn in the track hematite-stained greywackes, tuffs and thin mudstones dipping $75°/200°$ are exposed (locality 4, SO 403848). These seem likely to form the northern limb of a small tight syncline; the Geological Survey Memoir reports very similar strata on the north side of Wart Hill dipping northwards. The hematite-stained rocks are thought to correlate with similar southerly dipping ones, which include an andesite, on the south side of the hill and in the stream at Round Oak (SO 397845). This supports a likely anticlinal structure for Wart Hill and suggests that the hematite-stained andesite, greywackes and tuffs are some of the youngest Uriconian Volcanics exposed in this inlier.

Continuing on this track an overgrown gully (locality 5, SO 401849) to the south may indicate the line of a small fault. In 1980 there was some evidence of overturned strata, unfortunately no longer exposed, on the basis of included shale fragments in greywacke. Exposure is now very poor but beyond this gully there is a different sequence of lavas. A banded rhyolite (SO 401849) is succeeded by a hematised andesite (the amygdales are hematite filled) and an amygdaloidal basalt. The rhyolite is no longer exposed but a careful search for the andesite should at least reveal fragments. The basalt (locality 6) crops out on a turn in the track. Although there are no more exposures, continue to the end of the track (SO 400850). The west side of the hill is bounded by a fault juxtaposing the Uriconian Volcanic Group with Wentnor Group strata.

Wentnor Group

Return along the track, to the site of the fault (locality 2) described earlier. To the east is a steep, hazardous descent (take care) to a stream that flows through Urwicks Wood in a northeasterly direction. In the bed of the stream are steeply dipping coarse-grained purple, micaceous sandstones with conglomeratic horizons. On the basis of lithology and structural relations these are placed in the Precambrian Longmyndian Supergroup. They are very similar to Wentnor Group (Bayston-Oakwood Formation) sandstones, exposed 11km north of here, which represent braided river deposits (Pauley, 1990). To explain the occurrence of these sandstones here, and at other localities within the Church Stretton Fault System, requires extensive Wentnor Group sedimentation over the area of the Church Stretton Fault zone in very late Precambrian times.

Return to the access gate and stile. A footpath on the south side of the road and 50 metres east of the access point to Wart Hill leads onto Hopesay Common (SO 398835)l. This broad ridge is the continuation southwards of the fault-bounded wedge of Wentnor Group sandstones. Fragments of coarse-grained purple sandstone can be found in the track leading onto the top of the ridge. There are no exposures on Hopesay Common but this location offers a pleasant walk with excellent views, similar to those already described, before returning to the vehicles.

ITINERARY 3

THE PRECAMBRIAN, CAMBRIAN AND ORDOVICIAN GEOLOGY OF THE CAER CARADOC AREA, AND LOCAL DEVELOPMENTS WITHIN THE CHURCH STRETTON FAULT SYSTEM

Introduction

This excursion studies the Uriconian Volcanics of the Caer Caradoc area, the adjacent Ordovician sediments laid down during the Caradoc epoch and the local development of the Church Stretton Fault System (Greig *et al.* 1968; Toghill, 1990). Throughout the walk there are extensive views of the South Shropshire Hills and these views will be used to explain relationships between the landscape and the underlying geology.

Geological Sequence in the Caer Caradoc Area

Ordovician: Caradoc Series
Cheney Longville Flags
alternata Limestone
Chatwall Sandstone
Chatwall Flags
Harnage Shales
Hoar Edge Grit
unconformity
Tremadoc Series
Shineton Shales
Cambrian: **Merioneth Series**
Black Shales
Grey (Orusia) Shales
St.David's Series
Upper Comley Sandstone
Caerfai Series
Lower Comley Sandstone with
Comley Limestones
Wrekin Quartzite
unconformity
Precambrian:
Wentnor Group (Western Longmyndian)
Stretton Group (Eastern Longmyndian)
Uriconian Volcanics: Little Caradoc Basalts
Caer Caradoc Rhyolites
Caer Caradoc Andesites
Ragleth Tuffs

The Caer Caradoc Area

The area is covered by British Geological Survey maps; 1:50000, Sheet 166, Church Stretton; and 1:25000, Sheet SO 49, Church Stretton. The topography is covered by Ordnance Survey Sheet SO 49/59,1:25000; and 1:50000 Landranger Series Sheet 137, Ludlow and Wenlock Edge.

During the late Precambrian eon, around 570 million years ago, the South Shropshire area was probably part of a cordilleran, Andean style, volcanic arc system situated close to the Antarctic circle (Pharaoh *et al.* 1987; Pauley, 1990; Tucker & Pharaoh, 1991; Compston, Wright & Toghill, 2002). The area could have been one of volcanic islands on thin continental crust within a marginal basin. The sub-aerial products of this ancient arc now form the famous Uriconian Volcanics, which are well exposed along the Church Stretton Fault System, and also along the Pontesford - Linley Fault that lies further to the west. The thick sequence of Longmyndian sediments, which is found between the two major fault lines, is also of late Precambrian age. The early Longmyndian was probably formed in an adjacent marginal basin at the same time as the Uriconian Volcanics were being erupted (Pauley, 1990), and contains a good deal of volcaniclastic material. The later Longmyndian was formed after the cessation of the volcanic activity. The Uriconian Volcanics and Longmyndian sediments were then deformed during the Cadomian orogeny at the very end of the Precambrian. The Church Stretton and Pontesford - Linley Fault Systems were probably initiated before deformation, and as the main tectonic forces were transpressive, a great deal of tear faulting occurred during the formation of the main Longmynd synclinal fold structure.

The Cambrian marine transgression starting at around 544 million years ago produced shallow water sediments over the whole of Shropshire, including the well-known Wrekin Quartzite and the famous rocks of the Comley area, which include the Comley Limestones with their early Cambrian trilobite faunas.

During the early Ordovician Tremadoc epoch, around 510 million years ago, deeper water over the whole of the area laid down the muddy sediments of the Shineton Shales. Plate tectonic movements then caused the shore line to regress to the west to lie along the Pontesford- Linley Fault. This produced a situation over Shropshire whereby an almost complete marine sequence, with volcanics, can be found in the Shelve area west of the Pontesford Linley Fault, whereas in the type Caradoc area to the east no sediments were formed during the Arenig, Llanvirn and Llandeilo epochs (Toghill, 2000, p.55). Increased plate tectonic activity at the start of the Caradoc epoch around 460 million years ago, produced a worldwide rise in sea-level, and the Caradoc transgression of the Welsh Borderland occurred which laid down the classic shallow water sequence of the type Caradoc area to be studied in this walk.

A major tectonic event, caused by the collision of Avalonia and Baltica, occurred during the Ashgill epoch at the end of the Ordovician period and produced folding and major faulting over Shropshire. This, the Shelveian Event (Toghill, 1992), produced the steep dips visible in the Ordovician rocks of the type Caradoc area and also complex, mainly tear, movements along the Church Stretton Fault System. A number of minor faults were initiated as well as the Sharpstones Thrust and other reverse faults. Late Ordovician Ashgill epoch rocks are absent over most of Shropshire because the sea once again regressed to the west with the shoreline lying somewhere in the Welsh Basin. This major regression was partly caused by the collision of Avalonia and Baltica and the consequent uplift caused by the Shelveian Event, but also because of a major glaciation centred over North Africa which caused sea-level to fall worldwide.

The remaining geological history of the area covered by the walk is as described for the whole of South Shropshire, earlier in this guide. However, it is worth noting that movements, mostly lateral, continued along the Church Stretton Fault System throughout most of the Palaeozoic and Mesozoic, and were renewed in the Tertiary. Movements during the mid-Tertiary were mainly normal, downthrowing Silurian rocks to the west into what is now the Church Stretton Valley.

Location

The walk starts from Willstone (SO 492 953) (Figure 14), a group of farms 2km west of Cardington. The area is reached by narrow lanes and at Willstone there is roadside parking for cars and minibuses, but the start point cannot be reached by coaches. The walk includes an ascent to the summit of Caer Caradoc at 459m. Access is along public footpaths and none of the route is over particularly steep ground although sturdy footwear is necessary. Access to locality 17, which is not on a public footpath is allowed by kind permission of Mr. Pennington of Willstone Farm.

Please do not hammer exposures, collect only from scree.

Itinerary

Walk southwestwards following the rough bridleway which is the old road from Cardington to Church Stretton (Figure 14). This track angles up the Wilderness Ridge formed by the Chatwall Sandstone and associated sediments. After 150m steeply dipping Cheney Longville Flags outcrop in the bed of the track striking at 30 degrees (Figure 15). They have an inverted dip of 85 degrees to the north-north-west. Please do not hammer these exposures as this will damage the bridleway.

The track climbs steadily uphill and after 600m at a gap in the hedge, and just before locality 1, there is an excellent view east to Willstone Hill and The Battlestones formed of Uriconian Volcanics above the Sharpstones Thrust, and in the distance can be seen Wenlock Edge and Brown Clee Hill, Shropshire's highest hill. On a clear day the view to the east extends as far as Dudley and the Clent Hills on the outskirts of Birmingham.

Walk on for another 50m, and just before the top of the hill on the right there is a quarry in the Chatwall Sandstone (locality 1) situated 650m uphill from Willstone Farm. This exposes purple, brown, close jointed, and shattered sandstones. The dip is almost vertical and strike 30 degrees. About 15m of strata are exposed and occasional shell bands yield gastropods.

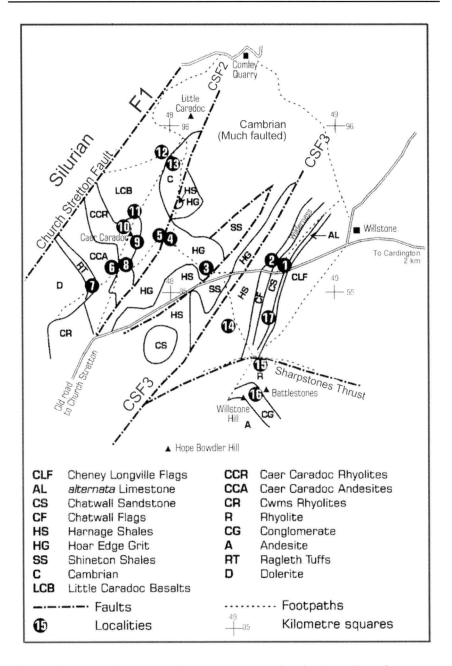

Figure 14. Locality and outline geology map for the Caer Caradoc area.

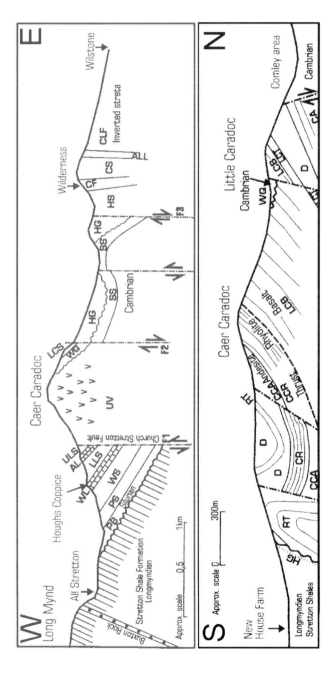

Figure 15.(above) East-west cross-section through the Caer Caradoc area. The line of section east of the Church Stretton Fault (branch F2) is along the itinerary route, localities 1 to 4. The section west of F2 is across the northern slope of Caer Caradoc showing the Cambrian unconformable on Uriconian Volcanics. The Church Stretton Valley is not a rift valley as the main fault (F1) simply downthrows (about 1km) Silurian rocks to the west where they rest unconformably on Longmyndian rocks in the floor of the valley. PB, Pentamerus beds; PS, Purple Shales; WS, Wenlock Shales; WL, Wenlock Limestone; LLS, Lower Ludlow Shales; AL, Aymestry Limestone; ULS, Upper Ludlow Shales; UV, Uriconian Volcanics; WQ, Wrekin Quartzite; LCS, Lower Comley Sandstone; SS, Shineton Shales; HG, Hoar Edge Grit; HS, Harnage Shales; CF, Chatwall Flags; CS, Chatwall Sandstone; ALL, alternata Limestone; CLF, Cheney Longville Flags.

Figure 16. (below) North-south cross-section through Caer Caradoc as seen from the viewpoint at locality 2. The Uriconian Volcanics vary in type from rhyolites through to andesites and basalts. CA, Comley Andesites; LCT, Little Caradoc Tuffs; LCB, Little Caradoc Basalts; CCR, Caer Caradoc Rhyolites; CCA, Caer Caradoc Andesites; CR, Cwms Rhyolites; RT, Ragleth Tuffs; D, dolerite; HG, Helmeth Grits; WQ, Wrekin Quartzite.

Continue for another 50m along the track from the quarry to the top of the hill and turn right over a stile by gate and walk northwards out onto the Wilderness Ridge for 70m to see the extensive view of the Caer Caradoc area (locality 2). From here the structure of Caer Caradoc as shown in Figure 16 can be appreciated as the view is towards this N-S cross section.

This viewpoint is on a ridge of Chatwall Sandstone, which extends northwards towards Chatwall itself. Immediately to the west is a complicated faulted area of Cambrian and lower Ordovician rocks between faults F2 and F3 of the Church Stretton Fault System. Immediately to the west is a small valley occupied by soft Harnage Shales and followed by fault F3 with a small ridge of Hoar Edge Grit behind. Robins Tump, an isolated outcrop of middle Cambrian strata, is obvious below the viewpoint. Caer Caradoc itself is made up of Uriconian Volcanics and fault F2 follows the obvious change in slope and vegetation trending north-south below the conspicuous summit ridge. The Comley area with its famous Cambrian exposures lies at the north end of the Caer Caradoc ridge between Little Caradoc and The Lawley, which is the next obvious Uriconian volcanic hill to the north. To the east of The Lawley, Cambrian sediments and the Shineton Shales occupy the low ground between it and the wooded escarpment of Hoar Edge with its basal Caradoc age sandstones. Between Little Caradoc and The Lawley there is a view northwest to the lower lying area of the Shropshire Plain formed of late Carboniferous sediments and, in particular, Permian and Triassic sediments. The Wrekin can be seen just to the right of Hoar Edge.

Return to the track and continue downhill for 120m passing exposures of the Chatwall Sandstone and Chatwall Flags. The dips here are very steep and the strike varies between 70 and 40 degrees. The track now descends into a small muddy valley formed by the Harnage Shales. Fault F3 crosses the track which now rises over a small ridge of Hoar Edge Grit (Figure 15). After passing up this slight slope for 80m the track now passes downhill westwards where, after 50m, a gate is reached. Pass through this gate and continue for another 50m and then turn right to the west over a stile by the gate and out onto the open hillside. This low ground is occupied by the Shineton Shales which stretch north towards the Comley area. From here there is a lovely view north towards Robins Tump and The Lawley, the Shropshire Plain and Hoar Edge.

Keep left and walk west for 400m along a rough cart track to reach a poor exposure of Hoar Edge Grit at locality 3. This is a coarse grained, quartz-rich sandstone, which dips 30 degrees to the west, and contains the moulds of brachiopods. We have now passed of the axis of a faulted anticline (Figure 15) with a core of Shineton Shales and Hoar Edge Grit on either side. The Hoar Edge Grit marks the base of the Caradoc sequence east of the Pontesford-Linley Fault and here rests with a marked unconformity on the basal Ordovician (Tremadoc Series) Shineton Shales and older strata. In this area of Shropshire there are no Arenig, Llanvirn or Llandeilo sediments within the Ordovician sequence. After the deposition of the Shineton Shales the area became a landmass for 30 million years before the onset of the Caradoc transgression.

The Hoar Edge Grit contains well rounded, sometimes frosted, grains of quartz and is a shallow water marine sandstone reworked on a desert shoreline area. Occasional large three-edged pebbles of polished quartz called driekanter indicate derivation from a wind blown desert area. The basal Caradoc transgression took place over a very irregular land surface and nearby, at Hazler Hill near Church Stretton, neptunean dykes of Caradoc age occur in Uriconian Volcanics indicating an ancient wave cut platform.

Follow the track WSW and then W as it curves right up a broad slope towards the obvious ridge of Caer Caradoc. This track is on well-drained ground of the Hoar Edge Grit, but notice to left, to the southwest, the boggy area of Harnage Shales and the obvious spring line where these occur against the Hoar Edge Grit.

Walk northwest for 600m towards the ridge of Caer Caradoc to a gate and stile at the base of the northern steep slope of the summit ridge. This stile is just about on Fault F2 where the Hoar Edge Grit is faulted against Uriconian Volcanics, and notice here the obvious change in slope as you cross the fault and the change in vegetation. About 80m before the stile, at the top of this broad slope, is a small exposure (locality 4) of Hoar Edge Grit which here is a pale whitish brown quartz feldspar sandstone dipping gently to the south. Hoar Edge Grit underlies all the broad slope which has just been ascended.

Cross the stile and walk 50m up the steep slope to where the path up Caer

Figure 17. 'Murchison's View' looking northeast from Caer Caradoc from locality 5. The prominent smooth-surfaced hill is The Lawley, with The Wrekin in the far distance. The Church Stretton Fault lies near the foot of the left-hand slopes of The Lawley and downthrows Carboniferous strata of the Leebotwood Coalfield. At the foot of the right-hand slope is the Cambrian unconformity, succeeded by prominent scarps developed in Ordovician Hoar Edge Grits and the Chatwall Sandstone.

Caradoc turns sharp left and angles SW up the slope. From here (locality 5) there's an excellent view to the north towards The Lawley, The Wrekin, Hoar Edge, and the associated Ordovician and Silurian scarp and vale scenery. This view was featured by Murchison in his *Silurian System* (Figure 17). You can also look back from here to the ground already covered and notice the obvious escarpments and valleys within the Caradoc age sequence. The view east shows The Battlestones, Willstone and Hope Bowdler Hills above the Sharpstones Thrust, all formed of Uriconian Volcanics. Further to the east is the Silurian escarpment of Wenlock Edge, and the Clee Hills capped by Coal Measures and a Carboniferous dolerite sill forming Titterstone Clee Hill and Brown Clee Hill, the latter the highest hill in Shropshire.

Walk up the track which angles up to the steep summit ridge of Caer Caradoc. Notice the boggy ground below, to the east, occupied by Harnage Shales around Cwms Cottage. Also notice the crags of rhyolite above the track. From this track there are excellent views south and west towards the Uriconian Volcanics of Hope Bowdler Hill, with the Gaer Stone crag of rhyolite at its southern end, and Helmeth Hill, Hazler Hill and Ragleth Hill, as well as the Silurian escarpments of the Wenlock Edge area. Directly below to the southeast is the Cwms area, a complicated area of Ordovician and Cambrian rocks, made famous by Cobbold in the early 20th century.

At the top of the track you pass through the entrance of the ancient Iron Age hill fort, which occupies the summit of Caer Caradoc. Walk west for about 100m to the western edge of the ramparts (locality 6) for excellent views of the Church Stretton valley, the main Church Stretton Fault F1 and the Longmynd to the west. Fault F1 is immediately at the bottom of the very steep slope where it abuts against woods and open fields. This area of wood and fields is made of Silurian sediments down-faulted into the Church Stretton valley along the western side of the main Church Stretton fault F1 (Figure 15) where they rest unconformably on Longmyndian strata. Figure 15 shows quite clearly that the Church Stretton Valley is not a rift valley, as is sometimes stated, as there is only one fault, F1, which simply downthrows to the west. This vertical movement on fault F1 is of Tertiary age, but movements during the Precambrian and late Ordovician were mainly lateral with a good deal of tear faulting which could have added up to several kilometres of displacement. The nearby Pontesford-Linley Fault may have had up to 40 km of lateral movement along it during the late Ordovician Shelveian event (Toghill, 1992, 2000).

In this southern area of the summit ridge, immediately east of locality 6 and just to the north of the southern ramparts of the hill fort, occur good exposures of the grey vesicular andesites belonging to the Caer Caradoc Andesites. Walk down the south ridge for 200m from the edge of the ramparts, passing good exposures of vesicular andesites, to reach an obvious ridge of rock which strikes across the hill (locality 7). This is made up of very fine grained, water-lain, laminated ashes belonging to the Ragleth Tuffs, which dip around 55 degrees to the west and show very good bedding. Pauley (1990) has correlated these with the early Longmyndian of an adjacent fore-arc basin. There is a good view here southwest to the supposed inlier of Western Longmyndian in the Cwms area below.

Return north through the ramparts and cross to the obvious pink crags of rhyolite within the Caer Caradoc Rhyolites on the eastern side of the summit ridge (locality 8). These are conspicuously brecciated but further north show obvious flow banding. The fracturing may be autobrecciation caused by the hot material being deposited in water. The rhyolites are faulted against the andesites seen earlier although the British Geological Survey (Greig *et al.* 1968) suggests they underlie the andesites (Figure 16). Further north along the Church Stretton Fault System, at Overley Hill near to The Wrekin, these rhyolites have been dated at 566 million years old (Tucker & Pharaoh, 1991). There is some debate as to whether these rhyolites are lava flows or pyroclastic ash flows produced by nuée ardentes. Proceed north towards the summit and 50m south of the summit under the eastern ramparts (locality 9) are excellent exposures of vesicular and flow banded rhyolites. Some of the rhyolites are amygdaloidal with vesicles filled by chalcedony. Just north of the summit (locality 10) are further exposures of the vesicular rhyolites.

The summit of Caer Caradoc at 459m OD offers extensive views of the South Shropshire Hills and the great variety of Shropshire geology. To the west the Longmynd with its deep eastern valleys, locally called batches, cut into the unique 7000m thick sequence of late Precambrian sediments can be clearly seen, and the Ordovician Stiperstones ridge appears just to the north end of the Longmynd. Earls Hill, made of Uriconian Volcanics, can be seen at the northern end of the Pontesford- Linley Fault. There is now an extensive view north along the Church Stretton Fault System to The Lawley and The Wrekin, and the scarp and vale scenery of the Ordovician and Silurian sediments to the east of the Church Stretton Fault extending up to Wenlock Edge, with the Clee Hills beyond capped by Carboniferous rocks.

The view to the south continues along the Church Stretton Fault towards Helmeth, Hazler and Ragleth Hills and the fault continues south-southwest towards the Radnor Forest area. On a clear day the Old Red Sandstone escarpment of the Black Mountains and Brecon Beacons can be seen in the distance to the south.

Continue northward from the top of Caer Caradoc down the north ridge and soon reach exposures in dark blue-black vesicular basalts (locality 11) of the Little Caradoc Basalts. Some of the basalts are amygdaloidal with infillings of calcite and other minerals. Descend the ridge for about 600m towards Little Caradoc until a fence comes in from the right about 300m before the col between Caer Caradoc and Little Caradoc. Here, a track and footpath cross the ridge E-W. Follow the track for 100m west until it turns sharp left to descend the hill. From here (locality 12) are wonderful views of the Stretton Valley. The main Church Stretton Fault F1 is at the bottom of this angled track and the wooded slopes below are in Silurian strata. There are excellent exposures of Little Caradoc Basalts here and also 100m to the north. Unlike the basalts near to the summit these are not vesicular.

From here it is possible to divert from the main route and follow the ridge north over Little Caradoc and down to Comley in order to visit the famous exposures of Cambrian strata at Comley Quarry. However, nowadays, the quarry offers little for geologists who are not experts on Cambrian stratigraphy, although the sediments can be studied. Fossils are extremely rare though many modern workers have concentrated on microfossils from the Comley Limestones.The quarry is now a Nature Reserve owned by the Shropshire Wildlife Trust.

The main route now follows the track back to the fence and passes through a gate to reach a large pile of boulders of Wrekin Quartzite and other rock types at locality 13. This northeast flank of Caer Caradoc used to be covered with boulders of Wrekin Quartzite and the area is mapped (Figure 14) by the British Geological Survey as Wrekin Quartzite. In restoring the land the farmer has removed all the boulders to this spot and another pile seen below on the col between Caer Caradoc and Little Caradoc.

Follow the track south along the east flank of Caer Caradoc. After 200m the track is parallel to fault F2 and the boggy ground below is formed by Harnage Shales faulted against Wrekin Quartzite. Proceed to a gate and stile which leads to the stile at the base of the main path up Caer Caradoc and Murchison's View (locality 5).

Now walk back down the broad slope of Hoar Edge Grit (which was ascended earlier) and which leads to the bridleway and old road coming up from Willstone. At the end of this slope do not go through the hill gate back onto the track but cross the stile 100m to the west of the gate and follow a footpath SSE heading for the obvious crags of The Battlestones. Cross towards a low ridge of Hoar Edge Grit 100 metres away. Walk towards a small valley between this ridge and a low hillock to the south with a clump of trees.

Descend southeast down this valley with a fence on your left and The Battlestones ahead. The path crosses fault F3 and goes on to boggy ground occupied by the Harnage Shales. After 400m reach a stile in the southeast corner of the field.

Cross the stile into a boggy wood and descend for 100m to cross a stream by a plank bridge. You may need to divert a little to the north to avoid the boggy ground. Where the bridge crosses the stream are excellent exposures of the Harnage Shales (locality 14). These are almost vertical and strike NE-SW.

From the stream continue uphill to the southeast over a boggy wooded area of Harnage Shales. Cross another plank bridge and continue for 400m uphill and heading southeast towards a barn on the slope below the Battlestones. Head for the southeast corner of the field. Towards the top of the field look back to Caer Caradoc and notice the faulted area of Ordovician rocks between faults F2 and F3. At the top of the field cross a stile and pass out onto the open hill above the barn. Walk northeast for 50m to another stile behind the barn where there is an old quarry in the Chatwall Sandstone (inaccessible). This quarry is at the southern limits of the outcrop of Caradoc sequence rocks and is right against the Sharpstones Thrust. The Ordovician rocks here have an almost vertical dip and are thrust over from the south by the Uriconian Volcanics of The Battlestones, Willstone and Hope Bowdler Hill and have an almost vertical dip.

The Sharpstone Thrust is discussed by the British Geological Survey (Greig *et al.* 1968, p. 272). If it was a normal fault its downthrow to the north would have to be *c.*1300m - a figure which seems to suggest the structure is unlikely to be a normal

Figure 18. View of the hillside crag known as the 'Battlestones' (locality 6) looking northwest towards Caer Caradoc. The outcrop is of Precambrian rhyolites and rhyolitic tuffs apparently faulted against a fine pebbly conglomerate.

fault, particularly as it strikes at right angles to the Church Stretton Fault, which is later in age , and against which it terminates. It also appears to be a low angle structure following the contours around the northern margins of Willstone Hill. The age of the Sharpstones Thrust is post-Caradoc and it is almost certainly a late Ordovician Shelveian structure (Toghill, 1992).

From this stile walk uphill heading southeast straight towards The Battlestones for 100m to reach a wide track heading west. From here (locality 15), enjoy the view back over the area so far covered. The Chatwall Sandstone strikes NNE to form the Wilderness ridge escarpment, which continues towards Chatwall. From this viewpoint follow an obvious track west for 300m as it angles uphill, passing through a gate, to reach the crest of Willstone Hill. At the top of the slope turn east for 200m to reach The Battlestones (locality 16), a crag of rhyolite, providing more wonderful views of Shropshire (Figure 18).

The pink rhyolites at The Battlestones appear to be fine-grained tuffs, brecciated and cut by joints and fault planes. On the west side of the crag at the top is a conspicuous polished and slickensided fault plane dipping SSE at 60 degrees. 20m southeast of the main crag is an exposure of conglomerates dipping SW at 35 degrees and apparently overlying the rhyolites. These are the Willstone Hill Conglomerates which the British Geological Survey (Greig *et al.* 1968, p. 19) include in the Uriconian Volcanics interbedded with rhyolites and andesites, but which Pauley (1991, p.177) suggests are equivalent to the conglomerates of the

Wentnor Group of the Longmyndian. The conglomerates contain clasts of quartz, quartzite, feldspar and basic igneous rocks. The contact between the conglomerates and the rhyolites is either a thrust or an unconformity.

From The Battlestones walk northwest down the spur of the hill heading for a small lake in the valley below, and towards the ridge of Caer Caradoc. Cross further outcrops of conglomerate and descend after 150m to the gate halfway along the track by which you ascended to The Battlestones. Turn right, northeast, and return to the stile to the east of the barn below locality 15. Cross the stile just to the east of the barn and walk down hill heading NE towards Willstone. After 400m at the bottom of the field cross a stile and a plank bridge by a pond and then another stile leads to a track leading back to Willstone. At this point turn back west along the rough track for 300m, pass through a gate, and reach a quarry (locality 17) in the *alternata* Limestone. This quarry is not near to a public footpath and access is only allowed by kind permission of Mr Pennington of Willstone Farm. **Please do not hammer the exposures** but you may collect from the loose scree. Susan Beale has kindly provided unpublished details of this quarry which exposes about 6m of strata within a sandy development of the *alternata* Limestone. Three distinct shell bands (coquinas) occur, up to 20cm thick, crowded with disarticulated valves of *Heterorthis alternata*, within the mainly medium grained clean purple brown sandstones. Many of the brachiopod valves are decalcified. The *alternata* Limestone is interpreted as representing a shallow water, near to shoreline environment, subject to periodic storms, which threw up the shell banks which subsequently formed coquinas. The beds dip at around 60 degrees to the southeast although the western exposures are folded and affected by soil creep. Follow the track back through the gate and walk a further 800m east to return to Willstone.

ITINERARY 4

THE STIPERSTONES AREA AND EAST SHELVE INLIER

Preface

This area encompasses the eastern part of the Ordovician Shelve Inlier and the extreme western margin of the Precambrian Longmyndian block. The purpose of this itinerary is to examine the rocks of the Tremadocian to Lower Llandeilo Series of the Ordovician Period and their fault-bounded eastern margin with volcanic and sedimentary Precambrian rocks (Figure 1). At some localities the sedimentary Ordovician strata are fossiliferous, and derelict mine workings provide sites of archaeological interest from which good mineral specimens may be collected. Many parts of the Stiperstones ridge provide panoramic views from which major geological features of the Welsh Borderland can be appreciated.

This area is located to the southwest of Shrewsbury, on and very close to the Welsh Border, and extends 5km eastwards from the A488 Shrewsbury to Bishop's Castle road. To reach the Stiperstones turn off the A488 2km south of Hope (SO 343015) and travel eastwards for 3km, passing through Shelve hamlet, and then turn right at the Pennerley T-junction. One kilometre south there is parking at the partly landscaped Bog Mine (SO 357978), alternatively park 1km to the east of The Bog just off the minor road to Bridges (SO 369976, Figure 19). The main part of the itinerary is a lengthy but rewarding excursion into an area of outstanding natural beauty which includes some quite strenuous walking for as much as 9km. Appropriate care should be taken over rough boulder strewn ground, on steep slopes, crags and when approaching mine workings. A public convenience is available at Snailbeach. A small village store and the Stiperstones Inn are usually open in Stiperstones Village. Alternatively, most localities are within half a kilometre of minor roads so a less demanding itinerary can be easily planned. The Stiperstones is a National Nature Reserve administered by English Nature.

Specimens should be collected from loose material and hammering is discouraged, with the possible exception of a spoil tip at Snailbeach, which has been left with the intention of providing good mineral specimens for visiting parties. Please respect and enjoy all aspects of the countryside.

The OS Explorer Sheet 216 (Welshpool and Montgomery) 1:25000 and B.G.S. sheet "The Shelve Ordovician Inlier" (1:25000) are recommended.

Introduction

Rocks of Precambrian and Ordovician age are well represented in South Shropshire. They show some structural complexity having been involved in major phases of earth movement, mainly related to the evolution and closure of the Iapetus Ocean, which brought about significant folding and faulting characteristically with a northeast to southwest Caledonoid trend. Fossiliferous horizons occur in

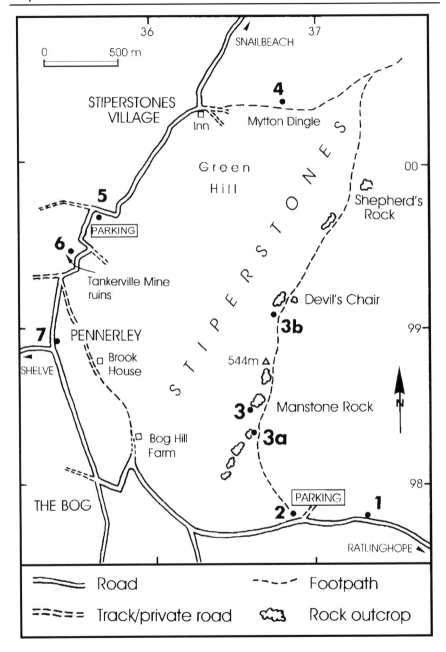

Figure 19. Locality map for the Stiperstones.

Ordovician strata and some Precambrian and Ordovician rocks are the host units for important mineral deposits.

Three divisions of late Precambrian rocks are recognised: Rushton Schists, Uriconian Volcanic Group and the Longmyndian Supergroup. The older Rushton Schists occur just west of The Wrekin and are garnet-epidote-mica schists providing a glimpse of the Monian-type basement that probably underlies Shropshire.

Like the Rushton Schists the Uriconian Volcanic Group occurs as upfaulted slivers and blocks mainly exposed within, or in close proximity to the Church Stretton Fault System. Uriconian Volcanics probably represent the fragment of an island arc system, consisting of a range of calc-alkaline volcanics and tuffs such as rhyolites, dacites, andesites, various pyroclastics and small volumes of basalt. These rocks are well exposed at The Wrekin, and on Caer Caradoc, Ragleth, The Lawley and Cardington Hills immediately east of Church Stretton.

Pauley (1990) has suggested that the sedimentary rocks of the Longmyndian Supergroup were derived at least partly from the weathering and erosion of the island arc volcanics. He describes the Longmyndian as a progressively shallowing sequence from muddy turbidites through deltaic sands to braided river and flood-plain sediments. Pyroclastic horizons within the Longmyndian may represent reworked volcanics or waning phases of island arc vulcanicity. The 6500m thick Longmyndian sedimentary pile is thought to have been folded into a major isoclinal syncline prior to the deposition of transgressive Lower Cambrian marine sandstones.

The Tremadocian over the mid-Welsh Border and Central Midlands region comprises shales, siltstones and mudstones suggesting a phase of monotonous, low energy marine deposition. After Tremadocian times there is a fascinating contrast in Ordovician sedimentation across South Shropshire. Within and east of the Church Stretton Fault System some 470-1000m of shallow water, marine sandstones, limestones and shales occur as part of the Caradocian Series, and contain a 'shelly facies' shelf fauna. The Arenig, Llanvirn, Llandeilo, part of the Caradoc, and Ashgill Series are absent due either to erosion, non-deposition or a combination of these. It has been argued that earth movements, perhaps related to the Church Stretton Fault System, may have influenced sedimentation.

In contrast, 15km west, in the Shelve Inlier, there is an almost complete Ordovician succession (c. 6000m thick) with only a small break at the base of the Arenig though, as to the east, the Ashgill Series is not represented. Sedimentary conditions must have been very different with considerable thicknesses of muddy sediment being deposited giving rise to shales and some mudstones. Contemporaneous volcanicity produced mainly andesitic lavas and a range of pyroclastics. Arenig times started with a shallow, transgressive quartz-rich sand being deposited, before the passage into the muddy and volcanic environment. With the exception of a small number of localities fossils are fairly sparse. The Shelve succession yields a mix of middle - outer shelf trilobites and brachiopods with a scatter of pelagic graptolites.

A phase of post-Caradocian - pre Middle Llandoverian earth movements known as the Shelvian Event folded the Ordovician strata of Shelve into the north-

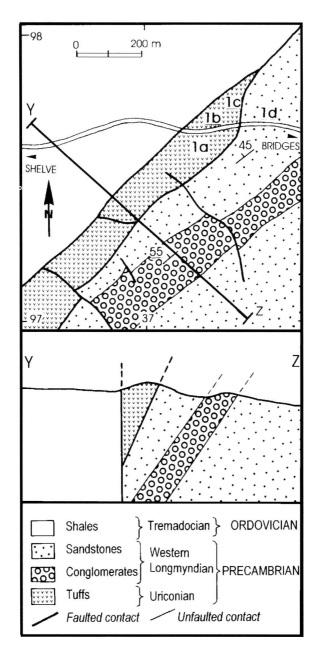

Figure 20. The Knolls.

east - southwest trending Ritton Castle Syncline and Shelve Anticline. The pattern of major and minor faults across Shelve e.g. Pontesford and Stiperstone Faults, and in other parts of the Welsh Borders, suggest the existence of strike-slip duplexes (Lynas, 1988; Woodcock & Fisher, 1986). Tear faulting dominates duplexes, and associated minor faults develop a braided fracture pattern. Dolerite intrusions post-date Shelvian folding and predate the Middle Llandoverian marine transgression the latter leading to the deposition of extremely fossiliferous conglomerates and sandstones resting unconformably on Precambrian and Ordovician strata.

The Ordovician Mytton Flags Formation has undergone barite (barytes)-sulphide mineralization and Western Longmyndian sandstones are also the host rock for barite deposits. There is clear evidence of structural and stratigraphic controls. The barite-sulphide deposits are mainly confined to fault zones and largely die out at the Mytton Flags contacts with the underlying Stiperstones Quartzite and overlying Hope Shales Formation.

Uriconian Volcanic Group and
Western Longmyndian (Wentnor) Group

From the car park (SO 369976) on the east side of the Stiperstones ridge a short walk of 250m eastwards, keeping on the minor road to Bridges, traverses the Pontesford Fault (Woodcock, 1984) (Locality 1, Figure 19). Although no rocks are exposed a small depression indicates the line of the main component of this fault which brings Tremadocian strata against a fault-bounded slice of suspected Precambrian (Uriconian?) volcanics that form a small, but distinct ridge, The Knolls (locality 1a, Figure 20). Ten metres west of a cattle grid there is an outcrop of these volcanics: pale, poorly sorted, silicified rhyolitic crystal tuffs (locality 1b). The cattle grid marks the position of a strand of the Pontesford Fault which is no longer exposed but is known to form the contact between Western Longmyndian sandstones and the suspected Uriconian volcanics (locality 1c). A few metres east of the cattle grid a deeply weathered, very coarse-grained sandstone with isolated pebbles was once exposed (locality 1d). Two hundred and fifty metres further east on the Bridges road is a small outcrop of conglomerate. This is a typical Longmyndian conglomerate with pebbles, many of quartz, quartzite and acid volcanics, having long axes up to 5cm in a very coarse-grained sandstone matrix. Return to the car park.

Tremadoc Series

The Habberley Shales Formation is very poorly exposed in the low bank on the north side of the car park (locality 2, Figure 19) and consists of micaceous shales, siltstones and nodular mudstones that are sometimes stained orange by limonite. Elsewhere the Habberley (or Shineton) Shales have yielded *Dictyonema flabelliforme* and *Angelina sedgwickii* (Fortey & Owens, 1992).

Stiperstones and East Shelve Area

Arenig Series

A very clear footpath leads from the car park to the Stiperstones ridge (locality 3) which is one of the dominant features of the South Shropshire landscape, rising to 536m OD at Manstone Rock (SO 367985) and extending for 15km north-north-eastwards from Heath Mynd (SO 335994), near Linley, to Nills Hill (SJ 396051), near Pontesford. There are excellent views eastwards towards the Longmynd plateau, and southeastwards the western Longmynd fault scarp is clearly visible. Beyond, and to the south, is the more rolling Silurian terrain with the Clee Hills composed of Devonian strata and capped by Carboniferous rocks on the distant sky-line. Westwards is the Shelve Inlier, where ridges are composed of Ordovician volcanics and dolerites, with shales forming the intervening lower ground. The very distinctive mass of Corndon Hill marks an intrusive quartz-dolerite phacolith. Beyond Shelve on a clear day the Welsh Mountains form the western skyline. To the north and northwest is the North Shropshire - Cheshire Plain, floored by Permo-Triassic sedimentary rocks.

The Stiperstones ridge provides excellent exposures in a series of large crags of the tough, thickly bedded quartz-arenite sandstone that forms almost all of the Stiperstones Quartzite Formation (Front Cover). Care should be taken when studying the crags and the rough, boulder-strewn ground between the crags. The latter supports a thin, acidic, peaty soil with a partial cover of heather and bilberry sometimes making walking awkward. Although the sandstone is well exposed, loose, broken boulders sometimes reveal more clearly the range of lithological variations, sedimentary structures and bioturbation features characteristic of this formation.

About 750m south of the cairn (SO 366982) where the footpath tops the ridge a low outcrop of sandstone (locality 3a) displays oscillation ripple marks. These structures are common on bedding surfaces and display amplitudes of 5-10cm with wavelengths of 50-90cm. Here, and in other exposures, the fine to very coarse sandstone is deduced to have been deposited in a high energy environment. Individual beds are well sorted except for conglomeratic layers, which are usually developed in the lower parts of sand beds. Various scales of cross-bedding laminations are faintly discernable and usually emphasised by differential weathering and changes in grain size. Mineralogically the sandstone is mature with a very small percentage of feldspars, non-quartzose lithic grains and shale clasts. Tabular shale clasts, or the sites of clasts where material has been weathered out, are usually concentrated at the base of the beds.

Some beds are thoroughly bioturbated in places. Vertical and *Diplocraterion* (U-shaped) burrows, the latter up to 20cm deep, are moderately common. Homogenised sand fill of burrows is usual. Other fossils are difficult to find, though inarticulate brachiopods and the trilobite *Nesuretus grandior* have been reported. When put together the mineralogy, palaeontology and sedimentology suggest deposition of the Stiperstones Quartzite in a very shallow water, littoral or beach zone. A silica cement finally produced an extremely hard and resistant rock.

Although barren of the economic minerals that were once worked from the overlying Mytton Flags Formation, traces of hematite and secondary copper minerals have been found on loose blocks staining quartz-coated joint surfaces (SO 367985, 100m south of Manstone Rock). Malachite and azurite are thought to have been derived by downward percolation and alteration of primary chalcopyrite in the Mytton Flags Formation. The hematite may reflect a Permo-Triassic red-bed cover since removed.

The Stiperstones Quartzite Formation dips steeply to the west and northwest forming the eastern limb of the Ritton Castle Syncline. The beds show small variations in dip and strike because they are off-set from each-other, mainly by minor faults associated with strike-slip movements along the Stiperstones Fault. Brecciated and fractured sandstones at the south end of the Devil's Chair outcrop (SO 368991) are evidence of this faulting (locality 3b, Figure 19). From the Devil's Chair continue along the ridge for just over 1km. (Do not turn west where this track is crossed at right angles by another which leads into Perkins Beach Valley.) Turn sharp left to meet a path alongside a dry stone wall that leads down into the steep sided Mytton Dingle (SJ 368000, locality 4, also known as Myttonsbeach Valley). Or continue north for another 1.5 km to Snailbeach where landscaped mine workings are safe and accessible. Alternatively, Snailbeach may be visited later after returning to the vehicles. A convenient car park and public convenience is available next to the village hall.

The steep northern side of Mytton Dingle displays good exposures in the type section for the Mytton Flags Formation. This unit succeeds the Stiperstones Quartzite Formation and was the host for the migrating saline mineralizing solutions (Pattrick & Bowell, 1991) responsible for the deposits of galena, sphalerite and barite that once made this part of Shropshire an important mining district.

At the foot of the steep descent into Mytton Dingle there is an accessible large exposure on the north side of the valley. A shaft here has been capped by a cast iron grid. The rocks at this locality are dark grey shales, siltstones and very fine to medium grained sandstones. These are well bedded, up to 60cm thick, with individual beds displaying fine internal laminations. Minor sedimentological differences in grain size and hardness of cement are emphasised by differential weathering. In bioturbated layers organic reworking of sediment has destroyed primary textures and laminations.

Evidence of mining activities are spoil tips, shafts and adits. Some shafts have been made safe by capping, but are ventilated to prevent the potential hazard of methane build-up and to allow roosting sites for bats. Proceed with caution, especially when leaving the footpath. A small spoil tip (SJ 370004) yields good specimens of galena, calcite and quartz, and the uncommon green mineral pyromorphite (a chloro-phosphate alteration product of galena). The footpath through Mytton Dingle passes several cottages and a large garage before leading into Stiperstones Village (SJ 363004). A small store and the Stiperstones Inn are immediately left of the telephone kiosk.

The Snailbeach Mine site (SJ 373022) has recently been reclaimed by Wardell Armstrong Ltd., but retains many features of geological and archaeological interest

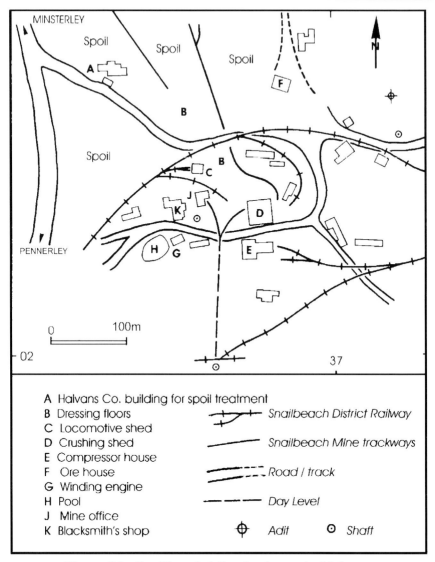

MINSTERLEY

Spoil

Spoil

Spoil

A

F

N

B

Spoil

B

C

J

K

D

PENNERLEY

H

G

E

0   100m

02   37

A Halvans Co. building for spoil treatment
B Dressing floors
C Locomotive shed   ┼┼┼ Snailbeach District Railway
D Crushing shed
E Compressor house   ───── Snailbeach Mine trackways
F Ore house
G Winding engine   ═══··· Road / track
H Pool
J Mine office   ─ ─ ─ Day Level
K Blacksmith's shop   ⊕ Adit   ☉ Shaft

Figure 21. Snailbeach Mine in the early 20th century.
The mine buildings are being restored.

(Figure 21). Mining at Snailbeach dates back to Roman times and the mine was extremely active during 1850-1880, finally closing in 1911. From the main shafts horizontal levels (or stopes) were driven to exploit the richest parts of the ore-bodies. Wagons moved ore along levels to the main shafts, to be lifted in skips or kibbles to the surface. Ore would then have been moved to dressing floors where it was crushed and the high density galena separated by running water on circular buddles and jiggers. Smelting took place one kilometre north of Snailbeach at Lower House (SJ 374021). Remaining spoil tips provide excellent specimens of galena, sphalerite, barite, calcite and quartz and traces of some copper minerals.

From the Stiperstones Inn follow the minor road through the village southwards, and then uphill for 0.5km to a hairpin bend. On the east side of the road at the start of the bend a small dolerite dyke intrudes grey shales of the Mytton Flags Formation (locality 5b). After the bend the small abandoned Bergam Quarry (SO 356997) provides a parking area (Figure 22). This quarry, an SSSI, displays vertical dark grey mudstones, and limonitic shales of the Mytton Flags Formation (locality 5a). A mudstone bed near the base of the quarry includes discrete ovoid lenses up to 20cm long and 0-5cm thick of a grey clay with pyrite crystals. This clay may be a bentonite perhaps of volcanic origin and the pyrite may have developed in low energy stagnant conditions at the time of mudstone deposition. Limonite staining seems to result from the oxidation of pyrite. The mudstones and shales have yielded specimens of the trilobites *Ogygiocaris, Ampyx* and *Trinucleus* and some didymograptids (*hirundo* zone). At the south edge of the quarry is the northern margin of a weathered dolerite dyke. A narrow baked margin where the mudstone is paler and more splintery can be seen when much loose material is scraped away. Small-scale but intensive

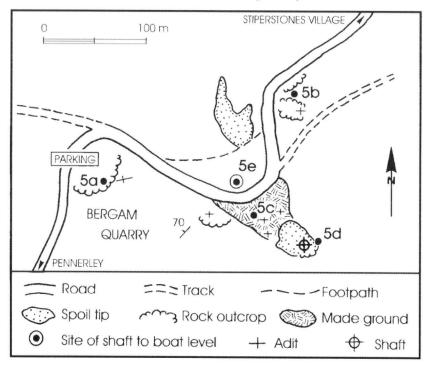

Figure 22. Bergam Quarry.

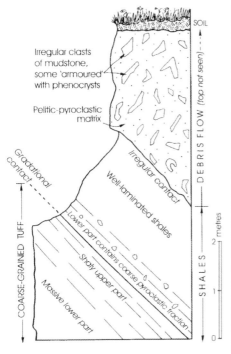

Figure 23. Tasker Quarry.

mining that marks the old Bergam mine is evident in a series of drainage adits (locality 5c), made ground and at the top of a steep spoil tip a sealed shaft entrance (locality 5d). An interesting archaeological feature is a depression (SO 357997) that marks the site of a shaft to the boat level (locality 5e), a drainage adit that linked Tankerville, Pennerley, The Bog and other smaller mines.

Almost 250m due south of Bergam Quarry are the remains of the Tankerville Mine (SO 355995, locality 6), once one of the major mines of the area. **For safety reasons do not venture onto this site.** Siltstones, fine-grained sandstones and shales of the Mytton Flags Formation are exposed on the east side of the road immediately before the pottery and mineral souvenir shop. From Tankerville the Pennerley Mine remains (SO 353988) are 0.5km to the south (locality 7) and, as with Snailbeach, good mineral specimens may be collected. From Pennerley it is 1km to the car park at The Bog along the minor road, or the same distance via the track by Brook House and Bog Hill Farm. The remainder of the itinerary describes the localities at Shelve Farm, Tasker Quarry and Hope village; the last two being next to the A488.

At Shelve Farm the Mytton Flags Formation is present in the form of a small anticlinal inlier. The beds are exposed in a small quarry, possibly cleared to allow for the construction of a new barn (SO 335990), and has yielded trilobites, graptolites and gastropods. It is an appropriate alternative to the well known, but now completely obscured, Shelve Church locality. Permission to visit the quarry should first be sought from the farmer. Please park at the roadside or at the farm and call at the farmhouse. Significant variations in faunal content, probably related to different depositional facies, exist between the easterly Mytton Flags outcrop, such as at Myttonsbeach and Bergam, and these equivalent beds at Shelve Farm.

To reach Tasker Quarry continue west from Shelve to the A488, turn left and after 4km turn left onto the minor road towards Nind.

Hyssington Volcanics, Llanvirn Series

After 50m park in the small lay-by on the left. To reach Tasker Quarry (SO 324956) walk back to the T-junction and then 120m northwards along the A488.

Exercise extreme caution as the roadside verge is very narrow. Tasker Quarry is an SSSI. Its floor is often partially waterlogged and the east face especially can be slippery. This face shows a very hard crystal tuff that fines upwards and is overlain by 2m of shales, the lowest 40cm containing broken feldspar crystals, which in turn are succeeded by at least 2.2m of a breccia (Figure 23). The breccia is interpreted as a debris flow, a chaotic deposit consisting of shale clasts up to 35cm long in a structureless mudstone-pyroclastic matrix. A small number of shale clasts are deformed and some have become 'armoured' with grains and crystals. The northern half of the quarry displays the following sequence:

Debris flow	1.0 m
Dolerite	1.2 m
Tuff, with a suggestion of deformation during flow	1.4 m
Dolerite	0.5 m
Tuff	0.8 m
Coarse-grained tuffaceous sandstone	1.0 m
Fine- to medium-grained sandstone	3.0 m
Thin, interbedded mudstones and tuffs	0.7 m
Tuff	0.9 m
Massive, thickly bedded sandstones	3.5 m

Hope Group, Llanvirn Series

From Tasker Quarry return to the vehicles and travel north on the A488 for 6km. At Hope (SJ 342015) turn left by the telephone kiosk where, just off the A488, is a small lay-by suitable for three vehicles. The Hope Shales consist predominantly of finely laminated shales with subordinate mudstones and silicified andesitic dust tuffs (previously called the 'Chinastone Ash'). The tuffs have responded in a rigid or competent manner to stresses responsible for the excellent folding seen here, while the shales have behaved in an incompetent way and display evidence of deformation and flow. Dust tuffs have developed radial fracture patterns in the hinge zone of the syncline, which is exposed next to the lay-by. Small displacements, up to 3cm, can be seen on radial fractures developed in a monocline 20m up the minor road next to the sharp right turn.

ITINERARY 5

THE STANDARD LUDLOVIAN SECTIONS
OF MORTIMER FOREST

Introduction

Although well known to Murchison the earliest detailed mapping of the Silurian strata of the Ludlow district is that of Elles and Slater (1906) who distinguished an Aymestry Group of Aymestry Limestone and Mocktree (*Dayia*) Shales succeeded by an Upper Ludlow Group of Lower (*Rhynchonella*) and Upper (*Chonetes*) Whitcliffe Flags and a Temeside Group of Downton Castle Sandstone and Temeside Shales. They also identified an anticline west of Ludlow with an axis plunging NE and a complementary syncline through Downton.

Modern work began with the founding of a "Ludlow Research Group" in 1951 with a notable field meeting taking place at Ludlow in 1958 (Allender *et al.* 1960). In particular, Holland, Lawson and Walmsley (1963) carried out a precise faunal zonation and applied the idea of using specific localities as "standard sections" or stratotypes. Thus their zonation systematised nomenclature using, for a Ludlovian Series, stages based on local place names Elton, Bringewood, Leintwardine and Whitcliffe. The fortuitous excavation of new forestry roads created several pristine sections in Mortimer Forest west of Ludlow, which gave further confirmation of this zonation (Lawson, 1973). The definitive account is that of White and Lawson (1978) in which three semi-continuous sections, Goggin Road, Deer Park Road and Sunnyhill, were described in terms of consecutive "collection localities" respectively totalling 32, 46 and 31. Finally, the deliberations in the 1980's for an internationally accepted stratigraphic column for the Silurian culminated in formal definitions of stratotype sections, both boundary (basal) and bulk (body) by Lawson and White (1989). Most recently the British Geological Survey have used the Ludlow area as their first contribution to the HOLOSTRAT venture and now available on the BGS website (Molyneux, 1999).

Itinerary

Since the original excavations and the heady days of the 1980's many of the sections had degraded and became overgrown. However, at the initiative of Shropshire and Hereford & Worcester RIGS Groups and using funding provided by English Nature the most degraded sections were, in March 2000, re-excavated and some significant collection localities re-vitalised. The itinerary, Figure 24, follows a route which will visit all the designated sections and starts and finishes at the Vinnalls car park (SO474732) some 4km west of Ludford on the minor Ludlow to Wigmore road. Along its length of 10km it follows, except for one short stretch of tarmac road, well surfaced traffic-free forestry roads and can be undertaken on foot or cycle.

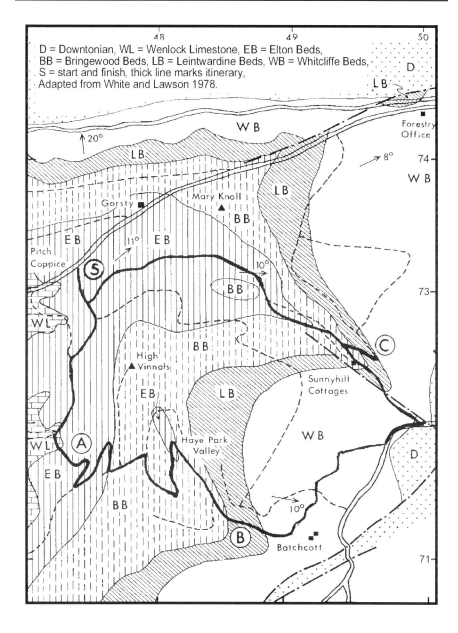

Figure 24. Locations and simplified geological map of Mortimer Forest.

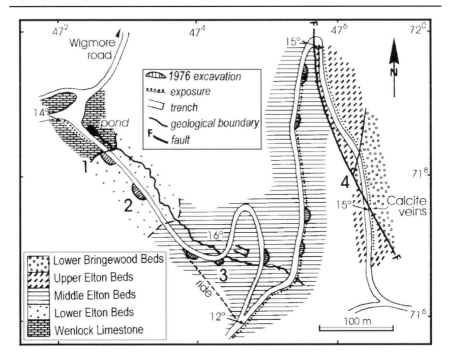

Figure 25.   Goggin Road; localities 1 to 4.

Ordnance Survey 1:25000 Explorer Map 203 (Ludlow) or Pathfinder 951 (Ludlow) apply. To follow the intricacies of the route these need to be used with care. The BGS 1:50000 Geological Sheet 181 for Ludlow is now published but the extra detail of the 1:25000 Special Sheet for Leintwardine & Ludlow is valuable.

From the Vinnalls car park head south but shortly bear right to follow a wide and gently ascending forest road with High Vinnalls on your left. After 750m this begins to descend and in a further 500m arrives at a complex junction with a pool and a conspicuous 3m high rock face.

Goggin Road   Lower Elton to Lower Bringewood Beds

Locality 1 {A1-5}
(numbers in { } brackets are locality numbers of White and Lawson (1978))

The rock face is of hard characteristically nodular Wenlock Limestone with a conspicuous shale band and a somewhat sparse fauna. To the left the excavation shows a transition to the softer calcareous mudstones of the Lower Elton beds. 1km due north at Pitch Coppice (SO472730) is the stratotype section for the base of the Ludlow Series coinciding with a sharp Wenlock Limestone/Lower Elton boundary. Here, the transition is more accessible and, whilst more diffuse, is clearly revealed in the lowest part of the excavation to the left of the low gully.

Lower Elton Beds are of mudstone variously silty with quite a high calcareous content (*c*. 40%) and effervesce in dilute hydrochloric acid quite vigorously. However, there has been appreciable decalcification, which can often be seen in a transition from a texture of white speckled shell fragments to brown decalcified moulds of the same fragments. Their fauna is of great interest and comprises elements which clearly derive from the Wenlockian. Brachiopods occur, such as *Atrypa reticularis*, *Leptaena depressa* and *Eospirifer* sp., trilobites such as *Dalmanites myops*, ostracods, corals and bryozoa with new introductions consequent on the change to muddier conditions, such as smaller brachiopods *Dicoelosia biloba*, *Howellella elegans,* and *Shagamella ludloviensis.*

Collecting can be something of a problem. In wet conditions these mudstones are quite intractable to handle on site and one can only collect samples. Adhering clay is best washed off by hosing and the sampled rock then dried. It can then be cleanly and reliably split to expose fresh internal surfaces for examination. Something of the great diversity and profusion is then revealed using a x10 lens or better a x10/x30 binocular microscope.

In general, small forms are well preserved. In particular there are Beyrichian ostracods such as *Beyrichia clausa* with its delicate punctate shell, smooth forms possibly including *Hemsiella maccoyiana* (but not here identified as such) plus numerous undecorated oval leperitids. Among brachiopods the small twin lobed shell of *Dicoelosia biloba* is common together with other members of a purported Dicoelosia community (Calef & Hancock, 1974), although these may be fragmentary. In addition there are *Gypidula* sp., *Howellella elegans*, trilobite pygidia and cephalon fragments, larger pieces of coral and various bryozoans. Fossil range charts for the whole Ludlovian succession which record the distribution of these and further species are published in Holland, Lawson and Walmsley(1963), Lawson and White (1989) and Siveter, Owens and Thomas (1989).

From opposite the pond continue for 100m along the road which heads southeast.

Locality 2   {A6}

Here the Lower Elton Beds are 25m above their base.. Their lithology remains unchanged but some faunal changes may be detected associated with a progressive rise in sea-level. Overall the fossil content is less profuse and there is a diminution in the proportion of fragmentary material. Ostracods are fewer but there is a tendency for the preservation of whole brachiopod shells. Thus, for example, *Atrypa reticularis, Isorthis orbicularis, Gypidula* sp. are now more easily recognised than in the basal sediments of locality 1. Trilobite pygidia and cephalons, mainly of *Dalmanites* sp. continue to occur but there seems a complete absence of *Dicoelosia biloba*.

Continue for a further 150m to where the forest road makes a left hand bend.

Locality 3   {A7-9, A10-11 and A12-14}

On the right-hand side of this bend is a cluster of three exposures all within the Middle Elton Formation. The actual boundary with the Lower Elton Formation cannot be exposed due to the intervention of a forest ride. The first exposure {A7} is crucial in showing in its lowest part a lithology similar to Lower Elton Mudstone but containing a graptolitic fauna. It is then succeeded by coarser siltstones becoming flaggy and only slightly calcareous and the exposure also shows a conspicuous 8 cm thick bentonite layer as a brown stained white clay. On the bend the exposure {A10-11} confirms the lithology as a grey flaggy slightly calcareous siltstone with a graptolitic fauna. Immediately to the left a deep cutting {A12-14} provides abundant talus with which to study and collect this fauna.

Conspicuous within the talus are flags whose hard siltstone upper surfaces are covered with a randomly orientated mat of graptolites. Preservation is poor but the impression of a slow accumulation of a pelagic fauna is strong. Splitting bulk rock usually reveals well preserved specimens usually broken to short lengths but sometimes of a quality to show the three dimensional form. The sediment often contains more fragmentary material, including obvious thecal spines from spinose graptolites, and diminutive shells of *Aegiria grayi* are scattered throughout.

Some 8 to 10 graptolite species have been identified in the Middle Elton Beds. Holland, Walmsley and Lawson (1963) found *Saetograptus colonus* to be common and the long stipes with rectangular section thecae are most easily recognised. *Pristiograptus dubius, S. varians, Lobograptus scanicus* and *Neodiversograptus nilssoni* require a degree of expertise. The latter two identify the standard *nilsonni* and *scanicus* biozones. White and Lawson (1978) identified two spinose forms, *Spinograptus spinosus* in lower beds and *Saetograptus chimaera* var. *semispinosus*, together with *Pristiograptus tumescens* appearing in higher beds. All, except *S. spinosus,* are figured in Siveter, Owens and Thomas (1989).

An interesting occurrence is the actual skeletal material of trilobites, white and calcareous, to be found in the freshest unweathered talus pieces. Mostly this is of *Dalmanites myops* but, except for pygidia, tends to be fragmentary. Also to be noted in this cutting are four bentonite bands conformable with the dip and separated from each other by about a metre. It is supposed that these bands derive from the chemical decomposition of intermittent volcanic ash falls whose source lay possibly to the south in the Mendip region.

Continue to ascend the forest road. Three hairpin bends occur, first to the right, then left, then right again, before the next locality. Obvious exposures at the second hair-pin and along the 400m section to the final bend lie within the upper parts of the Middle Elton Formation and provide opportunity to study changes in fauna. The track going off to the left at the final right-hand bend is a quick return to the Vinnalls car park.

Locality 4 {A24-31}

Past the bend there soon appears on the left-hand side well bedded flaggy coarse grey siltstones constituting Upper Elton Beds. These are separated from the Middle Elton by a south trending fault (shortly to be seen) which cuts out the actual boundary. The fauna of the Upper Elton Beds is sparse particularly with graptolites limited to *Pristiograptus tumescens* and marking the start of the *tumescens / incipiens* biozone. Also there is the small brachiopod *Protochonetes minimus* together with occasional *Lingula* sp., beyrichian ostracod and trilobite fragments.

After some 70 to 80 metres hard rock is suddenly replaced by a weathered and completely decalcified material yellow to yellow-brown, quite porous and of a surprising low density. This continues as far as the boundary with the Lower Bringewood Beds and this decalcification must have occurred since the original excavations in the 1970's as White and Lawson (1978) report the hard siltstone facies continuing right up to the Bringewood boundary. At least the latter is more easily found being where hard siltstone reappears at the level of the road surface (a point some 75m from a small wooden seat which lies ahead). Superficially similar to Upper Elton siltstone this basal Lower Bringewood Formation has a higher calcareous content, effervescing more vigorously, but diagnostically shows the presence of large strophomenid brachiopods and overall a diverse shelly fauna, although this is not well developed in this section. Occasional nodules and bands give an indication of the dark grey limestone to be seen at the next locality. Bioturbation is more prevalent in the siltstone often leaving traces of worm tracks on roughened bedding plane surfaces. The zonal graptolite *P. tumescens* is rare.

The outcrop continues for some 75m becoming gradually slightly nodular until, just opposite the afore-mentioned seat, it is abruptly terminated by a wide fault zone, heavily mineralised with calcite. This fault, trending NW-SE, is mapped as the same as that which cut out the Middle/Upper Elton boundary and here brings up a repeat exposure of Upper Elton Beds. These show a fine section up to 5m high in which the lithology is well displayed. However, examples of crinkle marks and slump structures caused by sediment slippage as reported by Holland, Walmsley and Lawson (1963) are absent from this exposure.

Finally, the view to the southwest must be remarked upon. The two inward facing scarps are relicts of an eroded anticline and their divergence results from the inclination or pitch of the axis of this structure. The two arms are eventually cut off 7km distant by a NNW-SSE trending fault lying roughly through Wigmore. Beyond this the anticline loses its identity and sedimentation becomes "basinal" and, once beyond the zone of the Church Stretton Fault System, dips are near horizontal. The most distant hill, Radnor Forest with its conspicuous radio mast, presents in this view a tabular sequence from Elton to Whitcliffe Formations.

Continue beyond the end of the exposure curving left. After 100m is a track to the left which goes to the summit of High Vinnalls, about 800m away, with a wide panorama to the north, southwest and southeast. Go past this track, crossing the line of the Mortimer Trail, and follow the main road as it bends gradually left to then make a sharp right-hand hairpin. This bend can be short-cut by a descending track trending east. The road continues to descend until beyond a sharp left-hand corner it makes a broad right-hand sweep across a wide valley to eventually reach a small pool on the right-hand side. This section can also be short-cut; from the above left-hand corner it is rough going down a steeply descending track which quickly turns left to arrive at the same pool.

Deer Park Road   **Lower Bringewood to Lower Whitcliffe Beds**

The small pool marks the start of the next section (Figure 26). In 30m is a small excavation on the left hand side.

Locality 5 {B1-6}

As a continuation of locality 4 this section of bioturbated calcareous shales looks equally barren of fossils. The trick is to find a band of actual limestone and one such band is present here some 0.5 metres above the base of the section. Some 4 to 6cm thick it splits to reveal fresh grey surfaces (80% carbonate) densely crowded with shells. Like many limestones it is the weathered and decalcified surfaces, which provide the more easily identified specimens. These now include as strophomenids the distinctive *Amphistrophia funiculata* and the flat fine ribbed *Leptostrophia filosa*. The spirifer *Atrypa reticularis* is most common and several forms already seen such as *Isorthis orbicularis, Aegiria grayi* and *Howellella elegans* are prevalent. Clusters of the small smooth shelled *Dayia navicula* put in their first appearance. Large examples to be found include the gastropod *Poleumita globosa* and the bivalve *Palaeopecten* sp.. Further excavations in what is the upper part of the Lower Bringewood Beds lie along the bank where they show a tendency to become more nodular.

Locality 6 {B7-11}

From locality 5 it is 100 metres southeast to a sharp left hand corner. In the exposure on this corner there is a sudden development of a band of mainly nodular limestone. A few of the nodules in this 100cm band show the shape and ribbed surface characteristic of the large brachiopod *Kirkidium knighti*, usually taken as the marker fossil for the Aymestry Limestone facies. However, as deposition of this limestone is known to be diachronous its appearance cannot be used to define a point in geological time which is a main function of a boundary stratotype. The base of the Upper Bringewood Formation is taken at a level 1.2 metres below this band where light grey calcareous siltstones containing abundant limestone nodules are sharply succeeded by hard light olive-grey silty limestones (White & Lawson, 1979).

Following the strata upwards, the nodular zone is quickly replaced by an interbedded sequence of calcareous siltstones and limestone bands, the latter similar to that seen in Lower Bringewood Beds. Further upward a more dominantly nodular limestone typical of Aymestry Limestone, as seen for example in its type section at Aymestry, appears to be developing, but is much obscured by a thick overburden of clay and soil.

Continue east along the forest road for 70m to the start of an embayment on the left hand side.

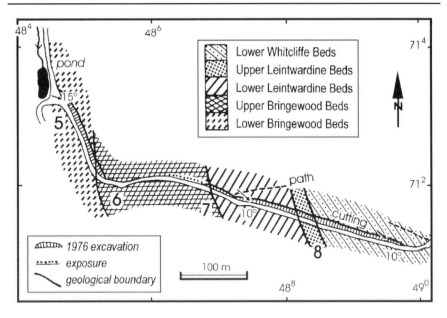

Figure 26. Deer Park Road; localities 5 to 8.

Locality 7 {B20-22}

The dip is ESE at 15 degrees so that this locality is higher in the sequence and it is therefore surprising not to have seen any evidence of "Aymestry Limestone" in situ. The reason becomes apparent at this locality, which is a deliberate excavation intended to expose the uppermost part of the Upper Bringewood Formation. Lithologically it comprises rubbly nodular limestone interbedded with shaly siltstones in a roughly 50:50 proportion. An example of the shaly siltstone is seen low down at the left hand extremity of the excavation beneath a heavy overburden of clay and rubble. Decalcified it shows a high profusion and diversity of small fossils of the Bringewood fauna. It even contains the turreted gastropod *Loxonema* sp. and, as is often the case in fine fossil rich sediments, a number of ostracod species. Weathering of this soft sediment must be partly or wholly the source of the abundance of sticky clay and soil in which are buried numerous rubbly blocks of dark grey limestone containing an impoverished Bringewood fauna.

At the right-hand extremity is an *in situ* exposure of a fine siltstone similar in colour and lithology to the above. Where it differs quite markedly is in its fossil content for this is the basal Leintwardine Formation. Gone or absent here are Bringewood forms and incoming are *Salopina lunata, Protochonetes ludloviensis, Sphaerirhynchia wilsoni* and the bivalve *Fuchsella amygdalina*. A new graptolite biozone, that of *Saetograptus leintwardinensis*, replaces the former one of *tumescens/incipiens*. Indeed the presence of the occasional orthocone encourages a search for this particular graptolite.

Although characteristic flaggy Lower Leintwardine Beds, with small brachiopods spread across bedding planes, are just beginning to develop in this basal section, overall the whole section fails to display the actual Bringewood/Leintwardine boundary.

Just beyond the excavation a track branches off diagonally to the left. However, continue along the main forest road and after some 70m the vegetation cover on the left hand side relents and there is good exposure.

Locality 8 {B31-49}

The Lower Leintwardine lithology of thin flaggy calcareous siltstones is now fully developed albeit largely decalcified and more or less bioturbated. There are bands of harder more calcareous material with flat base and showing transition to a bioturbated top. Fossil shells (casts) including the strongly ribbed *Microsphaeridiorhynchus nucula* (formerly *Camarotoechia nucula*) and the bivalve *Fuchsella amygdalina* tend to litter the roughened bedding planes although there are occasional coquinas of shells which were dominant at locality 7.

The flaggy lithology continues unaltered for 60 metres to a small cutting in the bank. The last 30 metres or so are in Upper Leintwardine beds notable for an increasing profusion of *Aegiria grayi* and the trilobite *Calymene puellaris* but effectively recognised by the presence of a large ostracod *Neobeyrichia lauensis* which acts as a zone fossil. However, there is better collecting from this horizon further on at locality 11

The cutting marks the approximate position of the Leintwardine/Whitcliffe Formation boundary. There is a detectable lithological change, the Whitcliffe Beds to the right being somewhat more massive. The real change is in fauna, which loses much of its exotic nature and becomes confined mainly to three brachiopods already seen and easily recognised, namely *Protochonetes ludloviensis*, *Salopina lunata* and *Microsphaeridiorhynchus nucula.* Indeed a Salopina Community (Calef & Hancock, 1974) or a *Protochonetes ludloviensis* Association (Molyneux, 1999) is often ascribed to Whitcliffe Beds. In places the three brachiopods may be supplemented by *Fuchsella amygdalina* and, where bioturbation is particularly intense, the wide curvilinear worm track *Serpulites longisimus*. The exposure continues for 150m ending at the beginning of a left hand bend. Follow the forest road round two bends to a barrier and go straight over. The road then begins to descend via two sweeping bends to the Blackpole car park. Exit to the main tarmac road, turn left and descend to the bottom of the hill and turn left again onto a level straight forest road. Passing pools on the right in 400m this reaches a barrier (signed Sunnyhill) and in further 100m a fork. Take the right hand branch, which in 150m arrives at the conspicuous face of Sunnyhill quarry. A short cut from the car park leaves by a footpath from the NE corner (picnic table). This soon turns north and shortly arrives on the above forest road just short of the Sunnyhill barrier.

Sunnyhill track **Upper Bringewood to Lower Whitcliffe**
(see Figure 24)

Locality 9 {C1-13}

This quarry and the subsequent track sections repeat the stratigraphy of Upper Bringewood to Lower Whitcliffe Beds examined along Deer Park road. The quarry presents the stratotype section for the base of the Lower Leintwardine and Ludfordian Stage positioned in the western (left-most) part of the quarry face at the base of two thin shale bands in a sequence of bedded nodular limestone. Some 5 metres of Upper Bringewood have been exposed with the remainder of the quarry face being Lower Leintwardine. The shales correspond to thin bentonite layers; further shale or bentonites occur in the base of the Leintwardine. It is admittedly difficult to reconcile this exposure with the shattered confusion of locality 7 along Deer Park road but it has to be conceded that it is a better looking stratotype!

Head southeast along the ascending forest road for 125m.

Locality 10 {C22}

This excavated bank reveals rather thick flags whose fossil content confirms Lower Leintwardine Beds. Roughened bedding planes are replete with *Dayia navicula* and *Microsphaeridiorhynchus nucula* with less frequently *Aegiria grayi, Atrypa reticularis, Salopina lunata* and bivalve *Fuchsella amygdalina*. In parts these flags are less decalcified than localities 6 and 7 so that it is sometimes possible to recover actual shells. Continue for a further 100m.

Locality 11 {C26-31}

An old quarry, Overton quarry, lies in the angle of the hairpin bend. This exploited Lower Whitcliffe Beds but the left hand (NW) side has been deliberately extended to expose the junction with underlying Upper Leintwardine Beds. This is positioned low down on the left where a line of springs lies in the angle between a bedding plane bench and a vertical face. The spring line suggests a change of lithology, albeit slight, and faunal content confirms a significant boundary. Below this bench coquinas and bedding planes are particularly rich in *Aegiria grayi*, the "zonal" ostracod *Neobeyrichia lauensis* and pygidia of *Calymene puellaris* and *Encrinus* sp.. Above, the trio of Salopina Community brachiopods occur diagnostic of the Lower Whitcliffe Formation. The latter shows in places an incipient "spherical" jointing, which can be characteristic of sediments homogenised by bioturbation.

This excellent "collecting locality" marks the end of the itinerary. To return to the Vinnalls car park retrace steps to the quarry and exit along the track to the right heading northwest. Cross over the stream of the Mary Knoll valley at the first opportunity coming out onto the main forest road opposite way-mark post no. 98 and turning right. This leads without deviation back to the area just south of the Vinnalls car park. In doing so a number of small exposures will be encountered, specifically track surface, small quarry and stream sections. These will give something of the flavour of the original geological exploration within the area of Mortimer Forest both in terms of dip and strike with respect to the Ludlow anticline and position within the stratigraphic column.

Supplementary localities:

12. Bringewood Landslip SO474738.

In 1947, on the northwest facing dip slope, a 50 metre wide zone of Upper Bringewood Beds slipped down a single bedding plane whose dip coincided with the angle of slope.

Tension cracks and indications of a lubricating layer of shale are still visible.

13. Aymestry Main Quarry SO423655

The type locality for the Aymestry Limestone having a sharp contact with overlying Lower Leintwardine Flags. The limestone wedges out when traced westwards being replaced by grey "basinal" siltstones.

ITINERARY 6

MID SHELF SILURIAN STRATIGRAPHY
(Eaton, Harton & Diddlebury)

Introduction

Within South Shropshire the 24km long unbroken escarpment of Wenlock Edge from Craven Arms northeastwards to Much Wenlock is perhaps its most distinguished topographical feature (Figure 27). As can be seen from the 1:50000 geological map (Church Stretton sheet 166) the scarp is an expression of a regional dip to the southeast, typically of 10 degrees. Beginning with Ordovician strata near Church Stretton this SE dip extends as far as Carboniferous strata on Clee Hills and produces at least five parallel scarps of the harder rocks with intervening valleys excavated in softer sediments. This itinerary will explore the escarpments of the Wenlock and succeeding Aymestry Limestones and the three associated vales of Apedale, Hopedale and Corvedale.

Whereas itinerary 5 was concerned only with defining boundaries of litho- and bio-stratigraphic units within a small area and narrow geological context this itinerary, and itinerary 7, are broader in scope and partly concern the practicalities of large area and predominantly lithostratigraphical mapping. Thus Figure 28 juxtaposes the relevant part of the stratigraphic column of sheet 166 with a bio-stratigraphic classification of the Silurian Wenlock and Ludlow Series.

Figure 27. View looking eastwards from near Craven Arms across the Wenlock Shale topography to the limestone escarpment of Wenlock Edge. Behind is the higher, but more discontinuous, escarpment of Aymestry Group limestones.

SERIES	FORMATION	MEMBER	BGS Map Sheet 166
Pridoli	Ledbury		Ledbury Group 457
	Temeside	Temeside Shales	Temeside Shales 12 to 41
	Downton Castle Sandstone.	Downton Castle Sst.	Downton Castle Sandstone 6 - 15
		Ludlow Bone Bed	Ludlow Bone Bed <<1
Ludlow	Whitcliffe	Upper Whitcliffe beds	Upper Ludlow Shales 30-122
		Lower Whitcliffe beds	
	Leintwardine	Upper Leintwardine beds	
		Lower Leintwardine beds	Aymestry Group 24-64
	Bringewood	Upper Bringewood beds	
		Lower Bringewood beds	Lower Ludlow Shales 183-259
	Elton	Upper Elton beds	
		Middle Elton beds	
		Lower Elton beds	
Wenlock	Much Wenlock	Edgton	Wenlock Limestone 0-18
		Longville	Tickwood beds 15-56
	Coalbrookdale	Farley	
		Apedale	Wenlock Shales 305
	Buildwas		

<------------------conformable on Purple Shales and Kenley Grit ------------->

Based on BGS 1:50000 Church Stretton sheet 166, Siveter et al. (1989) and Basset (1989). Stages omitted   Numbers are thickness ranges of BGS Stratigraphic units in metres

Figure 28. Silurian Stratigraphy east of Church Stretton Fault and in off-reef tract west of Easthope.

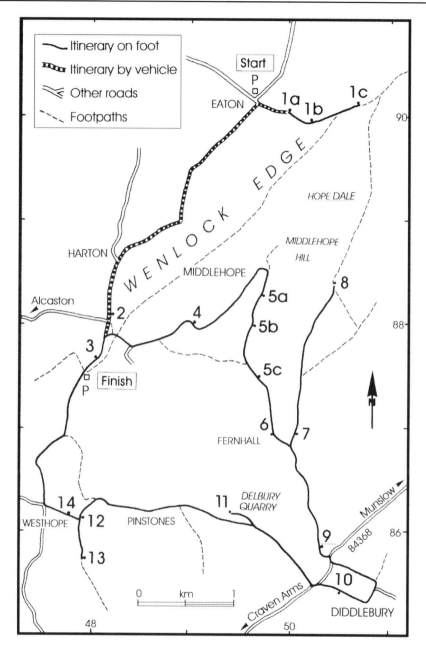

Figure 29. Eaton Harton, & Diddlebury localities 1 to 14.

(It should be noted that the Wenlock strata are in the so-called "off-reef tract". The famous development of reef structures is confined to that part of the Edge north-east of Easthope (SO556452). Such reefs can be seen at Ippikin's Rock (SO568965) and along the Heritage Trail at Presthope (SO583976)).

Itinerary

This itinerary, Figure 29, starts at Eaton (SO500900) and includes an ascent of Wenlock Edge. It is then convenient to travel (by vehicle) to Harton Hollow (SO480875) from where a circular walk, mainly on very quiet tarmac lanes, proceeds via Middlehope to Diddlebury and then returns by lane and bridleway via Pinstones and Westhope. Overall this walk, while not strenuous, is quite long (15km) but can be shortened to 11km by omitting locality 1 and even further to 5.5km by omitting locality 8 and terminating at Diddlebury. Requisite maps are either the OS 1:25000 Pathfinder sheet 931 for Craven Arms or the OS Explorer sheet 217 and for geology the BGS 1:50000 Church Stretton sheet 166 or, better, the 1:25000 Classical Areas sheet SO48 for Craven Arms.

Eaton is best approached from the village of Ticklerton, itself reached by branching south from the Much Wenlock - Church Stretton road B4371 at Hope Bowdler. Just before Eaton is an offset cross-roads with lanes to left and right separated by the abutments of an old railway bridge. Parking space will be found in the vicinity of the church and rectory which lie tucked in at the bottom of the tree-covered scarp slope of Wenlock Edge. A north-facing slope, almost total canopy cover and mainly soft sediments guarantee that this scarp slope will be usually muddy at all times of the year. Wellingtons or boots are essential.

Between the church and the rectory will be found the narrow entrance to "Eaton Track" (locality 1a). The track is used by horses as part of the Jack Mytton Way but conditions underfoot improve once it starts to climb. Past the end of the rectory wall the sides of this deep sunken lane show strata of the Apedale Member as a blocky fracturing grey calcareous mudstone or calcilutite, its monotony only relieved by sporadic siltstone and nodular horizons. To judge from the roughened texture of bedding surfaces it is heavily bioturbated, but fossils in this section are very scarce. Graptolites could be anticipated and such as occur are mainly broken and damaged, possibly by the bioturbation. After 100m a rise with bedding appearing in the track surface leads to a metal gate and a track junction. 50 metres to the left and over a wooden fence there is a Site of Special Scientific Interest (SSSI). Here, bank exposures yield trilobite impressions, usually *Dalmanites caudatus*, and solitary graptolites.

Returning to the junction continue along what is the main track. Graptolites become more common in exposures at 50 to 75 metres beyond the gate. The long range *Monograptus priodon* is present but the rectangular thecae of *Pristiograptus dubius* should be recognisable together with *Monograptus flemingi*. Such graptolites are part of the zonal scheme for the Silurian and 75m from the gate the boundary between lundgreni and nassa biozones occurs defining a "chronozone" (Bassett, 1989). The higher *nassa* biozone begins here with the disappearance of *Pristiograptus dubius* and appearance of *Gothograptus nassa* and *Pristiograptus jaegiri.*

The path now steepens appreciably, crossing a traverse track. There is an evident change in lithology to harder more massive mudstones of the Farley Member, which contain in exposures on the left hand side a very diverse although sparse fauna of scattered small, even tiny, brachiopods. Among these *Atrypa reticularis* and *Resserella elangantula* are most easily identified but minuscule versions of Wenlockian chonetids, spiriferids and rhychonellids can be recognised if not exactly identified. With shallowing waters a lithology of alternating and tabular siltstones and limestone bands begins to develop which correspond to the Tickwood Beds of the British Geological Survey. This character is shown in an exposure (locality 1b) at the next crossing track where yellow clay also suggests the presence of bentonite horizons.

In similar fashion there is a low exposure of the nodular Wenlock Limestone facies (locality 1c) where the path finally reaches the scarp crest. The dip slope of Wenlock Limestone tends to be quite narrow, typically 500 metres wide. Here it is effectively absent altogether being replaced by a col and dry valley at the head of Hopedale.

Return to Eaton church, retrace the route to the offset cross-roads and take the unsigned left branch heading southwest. This runs along Apedale with the Edge continuing to block all views to the southeast. At a T-junction reached in about 2km bear left so as to approach the Edge again. Park any vehicle on the verge opposite where a lane to Alcaston goes off to the right. An old stony track branches off left into the trees and arrives at the quarry of locality 2 in 50m. At roughly the same horizon in the lower part of Tickwood Beds as locality 1b this quarry shows a deeper section through the characteristic roughly tabular alternation of grey argillaceous limestone with grey and buff (decalcified) calcareous siltstone. The limestone is beginning to split with vertical joints showing the beginnings of boudin formation whilst the siltstone shows varying degrees of lamination. Unlike the underlying Farley Member the Tickwood Beds are almost devoid of fossils, just the occasional brachiopod and crinoid columnal. Small graptolite fragments have been recovered, too indistinct to identify.

Proceed now to the top of the scarp where vehicles may be parked in a car park for a Nature Reserve on the left-hand side. A height restriction of 6 feet (1.8 metres) applies but verges can provide alternatives. The itinerary now continues on foot returning to this car park unless transport arrangements have been made for a pick-up in, say, Diddlebury.

Return down the hill where two quarries lie in woodland on the right-hand side (east). The second, reached after 150 metres is locality 3. It demonstrates the preferential quarrying of Wenlock Limestone for lime-burning, the siltier Tickwood Beds being left and their top now forming a platform in the right-hand part. Low down in the face of the nodular Wenlock Limestone an incut shaley band is developed around a bentonite layer. Above this the nodules are held in a matrix of pale khaki siltstone with a sparse shelly fauna. The nodules are interesting. Classed as wackestones (more than 10% larger grains set in a carbonate mud) or micrites (more than 90% carbonate mud) they show a horizontal banding in polished sections. Their surface can carry the occasional full sized shell, such as *Leptaena* sp. and *Atrypa reticularis*, together with other shell and crinoidal debris. It is the last, generalised as "pelmatazoan" to indicate substrate fixed echinoderms, which partly justified the appellation "Edgton Member" for this limestone (Bassett, 1989). In fact the pelmatazoan limestone only really develops in the top 3 or 4 metres of the Wenlock Limestone and is better seen in the upper of the two quarries, some 50 metres down the road from the car park. This, however, is very overgrown and some persistence is needed to gain access to an outcrop.

Continue down the hill turning right after 300 metres. At an altitude of 210m O.D. this is one of the lowest crossing points along Wenlock Edge. The road emerges onto the dip slope and follows the line of strike NE towards Middlehope. In 600m a sharp right hand corner marks the position of locality 4 in the left hand roadside bank below Preens Barn. Two exposures show a transitional boundary between Wenlock Limestone and the Ludlovian Lower Ludlow Shales unlike the sharp boundary seen in Mortimer Forest. The first exposes the top of the limestone, very nodular with some crinoidal and shell debris. The second, 25m further down the road, is distinctly shaly with only scattered nodules. Unlike in Mortimer Forest the shales here lack any notable fauna.

Following round the second bend continue along the road to the farm and hamlet of Middlehope reached in 900m. In these remoter parts there was exclusive use of local "stone" for buildings and walls regardless of its poor quality. Such stone was extracted "on site" here, for example, probably from workings, now overgrown, on the north side of the road. Later reinforcement of vulnerable corners with quoins of red Downtonian sandstone (Old Red Sandstone) from Corvedale is also very common. The road loops and descends to a stream and then heads south.

In this next stretch are three roadside exposures in the Lower Ludlow Shales. The first, locality 5a, on the left just opposite the last building (a barn), contains a Lower Elton fauna with numerous brachiopods including *Aegiria gray*i, *Isorthis orbicularis* and, most relevant, *Dicoelosia biloba*. Also present in some profusion are trilobite fragments, pygidia and head shields mostly of *Dalmanites myops* as well as well preserved Beyrichian ostracods. The next two exposures, both on the right-hand side and respectively 250m (5b) and 750m (5c) along, are not quite so prolific although similar. 5b has yielded graptolites in harder greyish bands and in 5c trilobites are common. Unfortunately, neither of these exposures are able to show convincingly the biostratigraphy which justified the Survey's assignment of the uppermost Lower Ludlow Shales to the Lower Bringewood zone (Greig et al. 1968, p.158).

From 5c it is 600m to Fernhall quarry, locality 6. The exposures are near to the base of the Aymestry Group and, as a facies, they would be identified as Aymestry Limestone. This shows appreciable lateral variation as will be seen when two further outcrops are examined later at localities 8 & 13. A whole range of lithologies from soft mudstone through siltstones to hard limestone bands occurs in an irregularly repeating tabular sequence. Weathering of the strong joint faces has revealed much sedimentary detail including rippled and minor eroded horizons. The limestone has the typical fracture pattern of Bringewoodian strata and has a shiny grey, wholly shelly composition partially recrystallised. The range and disposition of dominantly brachiopod species suggests accumulation as thick layers of shells. Most easily identified are the near spherical *Sphaerirhynchia wilsoni* and the deeply ribbed *Microsphaeridorhynchus nucula*. As locality 183-189 of the BGS they found other Bringewood indicators here including *Leptostrophia filosa*, *Dayia navicula*, *Howellella elegans* and *Isorthis orbicularis*, but not *Kirkidium knighti*.

200 metres beyond the quarry a wide track, to the right hand side of a sign "Acton Top", doubles back in a northerly direction. In its surface is a grey silty version of limestone which is quickly succeeded by irregular flaggy bedded slightly micaceous coarse yellow siltstones exposed in the track banks as locality 7. This transition to Upper Ludlow Shales is quite sharp. These basal beds carry a Lower Leintwardine fauna which can be examined in the banks and on bedding planes in the track surface which continues for a distance of 800 metres. Lost are many explicit Bringewood forms; gained are Upper Ludlow forms such as *Salopina lunata* and *Protochonetes ludloviensis*, bivalves such as *Fuchsella amygdalina* and gastropods such as *Loxonema* sp.. Casual collecting from this hitherto undocumented section yielded the above in profusion plus brachiopods *Chonetes minimus*, *Microsphaeridorhynchus nucula*, *Orbiculoida rugata*, *Sphaerirrhynchia wilsoni*, the bivalve *Goniophora cymbaeformis* and gastropods of the flattened cone "*Pleurotomaria* sp." variety.

Optionally the itinerary can be extended by following the track towards the summit of Middlehope Hill from where there is a superb view down the dip slope of the Upper Ludlow into Corvedale with its network pattern of hedge-enclosed small fields and beyond to Brown Clee. At a path junction turn left to another Aymestry Limestone quarry of locality 8 on the crest of the scarp. The contrast with Fernhall quarry is most marked. Mainly of siltstones the limestone bands are reduced to numerous thin 1cm shell layers or coquinas which are laterally broken and discontinuous and seemingly affected by diagenesis. Return to locality 7

The lane now starts its descent of the dip slope into Diddlebury and a cutting between rock walls begins to form. However, there are no exposures which would mark any transition, say, from the Leintwardine to the Whitcliffe Formation (as occurs at Delbury quarry, locality 11). Beyond Bache Mill unequivocal Upper Whitcliffe Beds, at a left-hand side entrance, show bedding planes covered with the characteristic assemblage of the three brachiopods *Salopina lunata*, *Protochonetes ludloviensis* and *Microsphaeridorhynchus nucula*. These beds also contain thin coquinas of the same species admixed with fragments of the worm *Serpulites longissimus*. Bioturbation is very evident in dense mottling and grazing trails in thinner bedded shales.

Shortly after this the lane steepens to the same angle as the dip. Whilst rock is exposed on either side its examination is not easy or safe so that the section is somewhat disappointing. Some recompense can be found at the bottom of the slope by doubling back along the lane coming in from the right. Two quarries (locality 9) on private ground show high (up to 20m) joint faces remarkably smooth and etched with sedimentary detail. A possible slump band is discernible in the furthermost quarry. Such quarries undoubtedly provided the building stone so evident in the villages and churches along Corvedale.

Returning to the previous lane junction there is an obvious section which is

Figure 30. The buttresses at the southwest corner of Diddlebury Church. The original building of siltstones from the Ludlow Series Whitcliffe Beds has been reinforced with Devonian (Old Red) sandstone and faced with yellow Downton Castle Sandstone of the local Pridoli Series.

mapped as just below the base of the Downton Castle Sandstone (sheet 166, SO504858). This occurs in the garden wall on the left just before the main road; for obvious reasons do not hammer or remove material from this wall. The presence of the Ludlow Bone Bed might be expected but the section is too degraded for this to be proven. Cross the main road, trending right, and go through the metal gate a little to the right. There is a further small outcrop of the sandstone. Follow the footpath ESE for 500m to arrive at Diddlebury church. The exterior is a good example of local stone used for construction and then repair of the outside fabric. For example at the SW corner are three buttresses, one of Ludlovian siltstones very eroded the other two now faced with more resistant Devonian (O.R.S.) sandstones. Between them original siltstone walls are faced with yellow Downton Castle Sandstone (Figure 30). The south porch has been refaced with Triassic sandstone and inside are seats of more local grey rippled flags.

From the church follow the road and leave the village along Mill Lane. In the bank on the left are outcrops of purple marls and sandstones of the Ledbury Group (locality 10). These can be examined via a stile about 150m further ahead. About 1 metre of purple micaceous sandstone occurs here in a state to be recognisable; the purple marls are totally degraded. Shells of *Lingula cornea* are common in the sandstones but

Figure 31. The working Delbury Quarry, locality 11. Preferential extraction of stone from the Lower Whitcliffe Beds has left a platform of less workable Upper Leintwardine Beds, all highly fossiliferous.

otherwise the main feature is the demonstration that the Ludlow/Pridoli boundary has been crossed and with it a change of depositional regime from tidal marine to fresh water braided river systems.

Continue to the main road where turn left and then immediately right along a lane signposted to Pinstones. This begins to re-ascend the dip slope but at a lesser angle than the dip so that it gradually descends the stratigraphic sequence. After 500m Middle Barn shows a fine example of extensive renovations with local stone extracted from Delbury quarry (locality 11) whose entrance is in 200m at the edge of trees on the right hand side (Figure 31).

Note; if wishing to visit Delbury quarry you should obtain permission beforehand by phoning

Mr. Alan Fernhall on 07779 465937.

The contactee on the notice board should not be used.

Please adhere to any conditions which may be requested.

The quarry workings are at the end of the obvious track. Stone is being extracted from above a distinct platform the vertical edge of which, some 4m high, is on the right hand side (east). It is the rock of this platform which is of most interest since on the basis of "honey-combed texture", due to the dissolution of calcareous nodules, and a prolific fauna it exactly matches Upper Leintwardine Beds in their type area (Holland,

Lawson & Walmsley, 1963). There are abundant examples of bedding planes covered with brachiopods but most intriguing are numbers of gastropods, which are totally encased in a shield of bryozoa. These have been figured as *Cyclonema coralli* but are directly comparable with similar specimens found in Ordovician Coniston Limestone and for which a symbiotic relationship between gastropod and bryozoa has been suggested (McNamara, 1978). Rock above the platform is clearly of Whitcliffe age, heavily bioturbated and with the less diverse Upper Ludlovian fauna and, as it happens, greater utility for local building purposes.

Return to the Pinstones lane and continue, passing through the farm buildings and taking a farm track which heads due east with fir trees and then a wire fence on its left-hand side. This follows a field edge for 600m arriving at a metal 5-bar gate where turn right following the hedge line to arrive at a wooden gate and entrance to woodland in 100m. For a shorter return to Harton go through this wood, bear right at a fork and descend a hill to Upper Westhope there turning left and immediately right to ascend back to the car park. Otherwise turn left before the gate and follow the edge of the wood into an open field and then to a barn built of corrugated iron sheet. To the left are a number of exposures of hard flaggy siltstone (locality 12). These beds are just at the top of the Lower Ludlow Shales and clearly transitional between these shales (to be seen again in locality 14) and the Aymestry Group (next locality). They lack notable fossils and owe their hardness to a coarser grain size than the underlying mudstones.

A wooden gate and stile gives access to a path heading south into trees and gently climbing for 300m to the large Titterel quarry (locality 13) on the left-hand side. This, the third of the quarries in the Aymestry Limestone facies, again emphasises its lateral variation. Here, it is a very calcareous siltstone grading into silty limestone with strong smooth joint faces, very massive bedding and a compact texture in which can be seen numerous stages in nodule formation. There is a rich fauna comparable with previous exposures but which is difficult to examine or extract from the smooth faces.

Return to locality 12, pass the barn on the right and descend the sunken lane heading WNW to Westhope. The upper parts of this lane (locality 14) show numerous 1 - 2m high vertical sections through Lower Ludlow Shales and therefore complement what was only seen as limited exposures along locality 5. The section is undocumented and has not been looked at in detail by the author.

The lane exits as part of the cross roads at Westhope College. Turn right and follow the tarmac lane north through Middle Westhope, bear left at the fork and climb up to the car park at Harton Hollow.

ITINERARY 7A

OUTER SHELF SILURIAN STRATIGRAPHY
(Plowden Woods & Edgton)

Introduction

South of Church Stretton the eponymous fault system (CSF) marks a boundary between two distinct landscapes. To the east is a cuesta topography with three parallel scarps of Wenlock, Aymestry and Psammosteus Limestones and their intervening dales. To the west of the CSF these scarps are quickly attenuated to be replaced by a much more varied topography created by folding, fault blocks and glaciation. At the same time above a certain horizon there is an apparent abrupt change in lithology, sediments to the west being less calcareous and losing the above distinctive limestones.

Lying south of Plowden is a single fault block with dips consistently to the southeast at angles between 20 and 40 degrees over a distance of 5km and which comprises a complete Silurian sequence from the Pentamerus Sandstone Formation of Llandovery age upwards through to the Downtonian Formation of Pridoli age. On the Church Stretton sheet 166 published in 1964 the Ludlow Series within this block is mapped as "undivided". When in 1994 the adjacent Montgomery sheet 165 was published it became possible to contemplate a possible sub-division of this Ludlovian component in terms of a new "western" or basinal stratigraphy. In applying the latter this itinerary is intended to complement Itinerary 6 east of the Church Stretton Fault System and attempts to quantify some of the changes, which occur across the line of this fault.

The stratigraphy of Figure 32 applies to both this itinerary and that of itinerary 7B.

Itinerary

The route (Figure 33) by road and footpath is almost entirely covered by the 1:25000 OS Pathfinder sheet 930 for Bishop's Castle & Clun or completely by the Explorer sheet 217. Geological maps are the two 1:50000 sheets for Montgomery (165) & Church Stretton (166). From car parking at Plowden (SO379877) it follows the footpath of the Shropshire Way to the village of Edgton where there are then two choices:

(i) return on foot to Plowden to recover transport, total distance 7km.

(ii) continue on foot to Horderley (SO408871) having made suitable transport arrangements at that place, walking distance also 7km. Irrespective of these variants the start is at the lay-by on the north side of the A489 Craven Arms to Lydham road at SO391873, 300 metres SW of the milestone at Hillend

The Silurian unconformity at locality 1 is spectacularly displayed on the hillside as tilted slabs of purple fine conglomerate or pebbly sandstone. Traced upwards

SERIES	FORMATION	MEMBER	NOTES
Pridoli	Clun Forest		inferred
		Downton Castle Sst.	
		Platyschisma Shale	
Ludlow	Cefn Einion 300	Llan-Wen Hill Wern Quarry	Upper Whitcliffe Group
	Knucklas Castle 100		Spans Whitcliffe/ Leintwardine Groups
	Bailey Hill 700		Lower Leintwardine to Upper Elton Groups
	Oakley Mynd 160		Middle to Lower Elton Group
Wenlock	Aston Mudstone 300	Edgton Lmst.	Equiv. to Much Wenlock Lmst Formation (?)
	Bromleys Mill Shales 300		Equivalent to Wenlock Shales
Llandovery	Purple Shales 140		Diachronous
	Pentamerus Sandstone 20		

<---Unconformable on Precambrian Longmyndian at base----->

Based on BGS 1:50000 Montgomery sheet 165 and Siveter *et al.* of 1989. Correlation with Ludlovian Groups is imprecise due to lack of zonal fossils. Lithologies & fauna will be discussed in the text. Numbers are approximate thickness of Formations in metres.

Figure 32. Silurian Stratigraphy West of Church Stretton Fault.

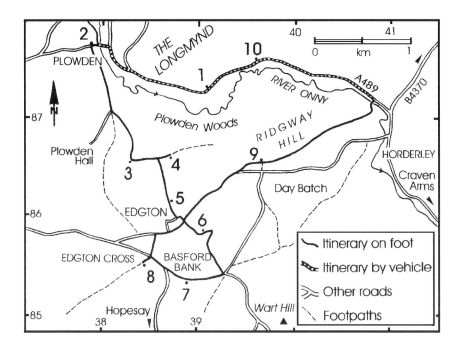

Figure 33. Plowden Woods and Edgton; Localities 1 to 10.

these can be clearly perceived to lie banked against vertical cliffs of steeply dipping indurated purple shales of the Longmyndian Synalds Group. On the small scale the actual contact is currently displayed back at road level low down to the right of the tree growing at the eastern end of the lay-by, where it shows complete absence of any faulting. **Please do not hammer these exposures. Any Silurian fossils are present only as virtually unidentifiable casts and this local occurrence of the unconformity is unique.**

As mapped by Whittard (1932) this unconformity can be followed from near Telford (as Kenley Grit) round the Longmynd and Shelve Inlier almost as far as Welshpool and shows features identified as pebble bars, shingle banks and sea "islets" or "stacks". The rise in sea-level or marine transgression, which is implied, was due as much to melting of polar icecaps of a late Ordovician glaciation as to tectonic causes (Loydell, 1998). The pebbly sandstone is quickly succeeded by fine pale grey shales which can be seen in excavations on the opposite side of the road and in the road bank on the corner to the west. These shales, with a small blocky fracture, locally develop bands rich in a well known smooth shelled brachiopod *Pentamerus oblongus* (which can be collected at locality 10 towards the end of this itinerary).

Continue westwards along the A489 noting on your right a field with islets of Precambrian protruding through the cultivated ground of Pentamerus Shales. After 800 metres the road begins to descend. Behind the ornate box hedge and cottage on the right is Park Plantation where Whittard excavated an old quarry to prove the unconformity and collected a representative selection of lower Silurian brachiopods. Shortly afterwards turn left into a minor road signposted to Eyton. If travelling by vehicle park in the immediate vicinity. This is Plowden. A lane branching to the right and signposted to Choulton leads in 150 metres to locality 2.

A major fault, the western Longmynd scarp fault, trends SSW-NNE and cuts out the Purple Shales (Figure 32) so that the bank is an exposure in the lower part of the Wenlockian succession. As a blocky calcareous mudstone it has the nature of Wenlock Shales but with an absence of comminuted shell debris (Bassett, 1989). It probably corresponds to the Coalbrookdale Formation which occupies the greater part of Apedale and the slopes below Wenlock Edge itself (see Itinerary 6). Thus the appellation Bromleys Mill Shale may seem superfluous! It is, however, worthwhile looking for graptolites; well preserved specimens of *Monograptus priodon* have been found here and at a similar horizon (SO345874) near Horderley.

Return to Plowden and by the school take the minor tarmac track heading south and signposted as the Shropshire Way. This re-crosses the scarp fault but all exposure is absent until after 700m the tarmac veers off to the right with a track and footpath to the left. A small outcrop of Wenlock or Bromleys Mill Shale shows in the track surface. Take the footpath which climbs to the SE and still marked for the Shropshire Way. Cutting through woodland this arrives in 500m at a sharp left-hand turn at the foot of a steep slope, possibly a scarp, with a quarry exposure facing (locality 3).

This exposure is another typical example of Wenlock Shales (Coalbrookdale Formation), such as may be found along the foot of Wenlock Edge, and comprises a blocky, quite fissile interbedding of fine calcareous siltstone and mudstone with a few harder nodules. Strong joints are developed trending along the direction of dip. Some parts show a tendency towards spheroidal jointing which can occur in homogenised bioturbated sediments. There is a marine pelagic fauna with orthocones quite common but graptolites are somewhat sparse, although there is a fine carbonaceous material resembling thecal spines. A conspicuous shale band encloses a pale bentonite clay, the altered residue of contemporaneous volcanic activity.

Turning left to begin the sloping climb to the top of the "scarp" raises the question as to whether this is a proper description for this steep hillside. It will be seen in the numerous surface exposures that the strike continues trending SW-NE (45 degrees) and is inclined to the lie of the slope and that the dip, 30 degrees to the SE, is rather too steep for a typical escarpment to form. More significant is that the lithology of the shales of locality 3 continues all the way up the slope and is only replaced by a softer tabular bedded mudstone in the few metres before reaching the crest. As this easily eroded sediment occurs at the crest this slope feature is not an escarpment in the strictly geomorphological sense. It is more likely a glacial erosion feature dating from the time a tongue of the Irish Sea Ice squeezed through the Longmynd-Plowden gap and down an excavated valley towards Marshbrook. At the crest is a path junction whose low banks are in a very degraded state; the much better exposure of locality 4 is found by continuing 40m east along the crest to where a further track begins a sloping descent.

There is sufficient exposure over the length of this outcrop to show a transition from the previous shales to an increasing calcareous but tabular or flaggy bedded mudstone. In the context of the stratigraphy of Figure 32 this is unequivocally Aston Mudstone and bears direct comparison with the type section in Aston Dingle (SO295912) on the northern slope of the Kerry Ridgeway. However, there seems to be more in the way of coquinas and less in the way of graptolites suggesting an origin in shallower current-swept waters. The coquinas are small and hard to find and usually totally decalcified to a rottenstone. Examples from here and in other exposures have included pockets of trilobites, specifically *Dalmanites* sp., and allogenic clusters of small brachiopods in which *Dicoelosia biloba* and small chonetids are prominent intermingled with broken debris of bryozoa and crinoid columnals. Occasional large full-size *Leptaena rhomboidalis* and *Atrypa reticularis* occur as characteristic Wenlock forms with infrequent solitary corals and gastropods. Well preserved tests of Beyrichian ostracods, probably *Beyrichia kloedeni*, are quite frequent and the material as a whole bears a strong resemblance to that of the Lower Elton Beds described in Itinerary 5.

Return to the path junction and take the route of the Shropshire Way in a SSE direction through a gate and over a number of stiles. Ahead note the rise of a second scarp-like feature in a position expected of Aymestry Group limestone. To the left there is the neglected remnants of an old sunken lane in which small exposures of Aston Mudstone Formation occur with a scattered fauna of small brachiopods. However, beyond the 4th stile alongside a metal gate at locality 5 these exposures comprise what could be considered as a proper hard limestone. Strongly jointed, nodular in parts with a full Wenlockian fauna of eight recorded brachiopod species, including those mentioned above in the Aston Mudstone plus corals *Favosites* sp. and *Halysites catenularius* (Greig *et al.* 1968, locality 47), this is the Edgton Limestone Member. The essential difference in the depiction of this facies in the stratigraphic column of the two BGS maps is now clear. Sheet 165 (Montgomery) considers the Edgton Limestone to be an interbedded member of the Aston Mudstone Formation with mudstone both above and below. Sheet 166 (Church Stretton) maps the whole of the Aston Mudstone as one unit and, in considering this the equivalent of Wenlock Limestone, labels it "Edgton Limestone". There are locally no more than half-a-dozen outcrops of the limestone itself of which this is probably the principal one.

Continue along the line of the sunken lane to emerge on a tarmac lane where turning left for 200m reaches the original site of the Village Hall of Edgton. The Hall was demolished in winter 2001 uncovering ground showing dark grey slightly calcareous siltstone. Continue southeast over the cross-roads into a descending sunken track in the right bank of which graptolitic shales may be noticed. **Please avoid collecting from here** but continue down the track across a stream to where the track bends sharply left and begins to climb the second scarp feature.

Numerous outcrops at locality 6 display the same graptolitic facies in a thin bedded sequence of dark fine siltstones. As will be evident this locality has been for long a popular collecting place (Moseley, 1992). Greig *et al.* (1968) noted four similar graptolitic exposures within the village of Edgton having a total fauna of *Monograptus chimaera, M. dubius, M. varians, M. colonus* and *Spinograptus spinosus* which matches that of Lower Ludlow Shales to the east of the Church Stretton Fault System. At this locality 6, and locality 8, the most common graptolites appear to be *Monograptus colonus* with its long rectangular thecae, and a spinose form with curvilinear thecae and spines, often broken, presumably *Spinograptus spinosus.* Comparison can now be made with rocks of the Oakley Mynd Formation. Oakley Mynd is a hill to the west about mid-way between Edgton and Bishop's Castle. Exposures are infrequent but a small quarry at SO336879 and a small track section at SO340881 provided material identical in lithology and with the same two graptolites present.

Final confirmation that the sedimentary regime is firmly set on a new course is found by continuing along the lane which zigzags over the ridge previously noted and arrives at a tarmac road with a stile opposite. In this section there are no evident exposures and equally no particular indication of underlying Aymestry Limestone. Just over the stile is a small outcrop of grey siltstone devoid of fossils (locality 7). Turning right down Basford Bank there are further outcrops in the bank on the left-hand side with some faulting in what is the Bailey Hill Formation.

At the bottom of the bank on the right-hand side beyond a metal gate is seen, on private ground, an excavation carried out at the foot of a small ridge. This has provided the most remarkable material. Interbedded with very flat-bedded thin siltstones are composite cobbles showing mineralisation, calcareous siltstone and large broken shells, amongst which the brachiopod *Kirkidium knighti* is most conspicuous. Above this are rolled boulders of calcareous siltstone with a dense fauna, often decalcified to brown rottenstone, in which the small brachiopod *Dayia navicula* is prolific. The material seems to be a combination of a mass debris flow overlying an intraformational conglomerate both of which have been noted (Cave, Hains & White, 1993) to often occur at the base of the Bailey Hill Formation. The source of such material could be shell banks and colonies accumulating in shallow seas on the shelf platform to the east, which broke away and cascaded down the shelf edge slope towards deeper waters.

It is now certain that the ridge trending SW-NE from here marks the outcrop of the base of the Bailey Hill Formation. The outcrop can be followed by the occurrence of fragments of the *Kirkidium*-containing conglomerate in soil and fields for some 1500m to where it is cut off by the Church Stretton Fault, near Day Batch. Locality 7 is, therefore, in the same formation but higher in the sequence.

From the foot of Basford Bank continue to the NW along the tarmac road arriving at locality 8 centred on the cross-roads known as Edgton Cross. To the left the narrow lane to Brunslow exposes further shales of the Oakley Mynd Formation. Turning right these shales can be traced in a section which shows their transition from the underlying Aston Mudstone and Edgton Limestone. On the left-hand side small exposures and the residue of a ditch dug in the winter of 2000 show, in a descending sequence, the graptolitic shales developed within an unfossiliferous calcareous siltstone (Aston Mudstone). Laterally, in the vicinity of "Stockwell",this siltstone is replaced by quite nodular Edgton Limestone, which occurs at various places in the bank on the right hand side as far as the entrance to Manor Farm. This outcrop has produced examples of the colonial coral *Favosites* sp.

From the road junction at Manor Farm turn right and return to the Village Hall

Figure 34. Disused Ridgeway Quarry (locality 9) with grey unfossiliferous siltstones, the upper part of the Aston Mudstone Formation, grading into the graptolitic Oakley Mynd Formation (to the right). The rocks are much affected by faulting, slickensiding, jointing and calcite mineralisation on account of their proximity, about 0.5km, to the Church Stretton Fault System.

crossroads where a return can be made to Plowden. The full itinerary continues NE along the road for 800m to branch off left along a public footpath. Ahead can be seen the scar of a conspicuous quarry (locality 9) which is reached in 250m.

Irrespective of its lithology Ridgeway Quarry, so close to the disturbances of the Church Stretton Fault, gives a superb demonstration of jointing, faulting and mineralisation. A major joint set trending 335 degrees (NW) is much mineralised with calcite and shows various amounts of movement, which become a distinct fault in the left hand corner. Slickensides show some movement to have been horizontal but with an additional inclined fault plane, overall movement was probably multiphase. In the centre of the quarry bedding planes (dip 50 degrees SSW) show a pair of intersecting joint planes so that the plane is divided into diamond shapes as by a conjugate shear joint set.

The lithology is that of tabular, flaggy bedded fine siltstone and mudstone much of which is hardly calcareous but some bands of which are close to pure limestone and recognised as hard, heavy with a clear shiny grey fracture. To the right, where beds are displaced by faulting these tabular strata become slightly more undulatory with a tendency for the limestone bands to separate into boudins. Fauna is extremely scarce but the brachiopods *Dalmanella* sp. and *Lingula symondsi* have been found (Greig *et al.* 1968, loc. 49) and one trilobite pygidium was found during a recent field trip. Stratigraphically matters remain consistent with locality 6; traced to the south these beds are quickly replaced by shales, which become graptolitic in a bank just beyond the buildings of Ridgeway farm.

The relatively hard beds in this quarry continue to the NE as a distinct ridge which has exactly the form of a "whaleback hill" expected by the erosion of steeply dipping strata. This offers a superb view which is best appreciated when its features are matched to the relevant geological maps, sheets 165 and 166. Follow the foot-path along this ridge and descend towards Horderley. As could be expected there is a return to Wenlock Shale with low cliffs of the Coalbrookdale Beds appearing. Beyond is the River Onny which on the right has formed a terrace backed by a low cliff. Proximity to the Church Stretton Fault has created a spring line along these cliffs and active tufa formation is taking place. The bedding is also affected by fault drag and becomes near vertical when followed downstream.

Cross over the river to regain the main A489 and recover any transport. Note opposite a deep narrow valley feature which, heading NE, marks the line of the F1 component of the Church Stretton Fault System. To the right the far bank of the road junction shows friable Precambrian Stretton Shales on the upthrust side of this fault. If returning to Plowden head west along the A489 noting the several outcrops of Coalbrookdale Beds and Pentamerus Shales. After 1.5km is an outcrop of the latter (locality 10). Although subject to much "erosion" from the activities of collectors this usually shows a number of highly visible shell bands. Persistence will be needed to recover anything other than brachiopod fauna such as, for example, the trilobite *Encrinus* sp.

Continuing west along the A489 it is less than 1km to the lay-by at the original start and 2km to the parking at Plowden.

ITINERARY 7B

OUTER SHELF SILURIAN STRATIGRAPHY
(Kempton & Bury Ditches)

Introduction

    This itinerary is intended as a logical continuation of itinerary 7A, which simply looked at the incoming of new lithologies and bulk changes in lithology for the Wenlock and Ludlow Series rocks west of the Church Stretton Fault. Since these changes are generally to less calcareous sequences, which become progressively thicker to the west, it is reasonable to infer that they are due to a change from deposition in a shallow water "shelf" area to a deeper "basin" area. Of some interest, therefore, is the position of the "shelf edge" which can be likened to the edge of present day continental shelves surrounding the world's continents. By plotting isopachs (lines of equal bed thickness) for each of the four Ludlovian stages Holland & Lawson (1963) were able to confirm a "basin and shelf as two distinct elements in the (Ludlovian) palaeogeography". The position of this shelf edge only partly coincides with that of the Church Stretton Fault System. Subsequently it has been possible to equate the basin with a SW-NE elongate "Montgomery Trough" whilst the shelf area itself can be sub-divided into inner, mid and outer zones across a wide extent of Silurian outcrop.

Figure 35. Typical slumped sediments within the Bailey Hill Formation in a small quarry along Stank Lane in the parish of Lydbury North.

It is a small step to perceive that sediment accumulating on the outer shelf could at times become unstable and suffer disturbances ranging from small slips, slides and slumps to wholesale collapse with the generation of turbidity currents directed towards the basin. The stages most affected seem to be Bringewood and Lower Leintwardine with submarine canyons developed at Leintwardine (Whitaker, 1962) and wholesale loss of Bringewood strata west of Wigmore (Whitaker, 1994). In Shropshire it is strata of the same age, represented by the Bailey Hill Formation, which is mainly affected. Slumps and possible mass debris slides have already been noted at the base of the formation (itinerary 7A). Figure 35 shows an example.

This itinerary first examines further slump features after which quieter conditions for the Knucklas Castle Beds were then followed by a prolonged marine regression during Whitcliffe times culminating in the establishment of brackish and fluviatile deposition.

Itinerary

Some 4km west of the Church Stretton Fault System the strata on either side of the E-W Clun valley are nearly horizontally bedded and provide a complete sequence from the Upper Bailey Hill to Cefn Einon Formations with, sometimes, a capping of Clun Forest Formation. The start lies just west of the hamlet of Kempton (Figure 36) where there is limited car parking space at SO356830, just short of the entrance gates to the Walcot estate. The best approach is from the Hundred Inn at Purslow on the B4368 Craven Arms to Clun road taking the minor road heading north. (The inn makes a convenient lunch-time break if doing both this and itinerary 7A on the same day.)

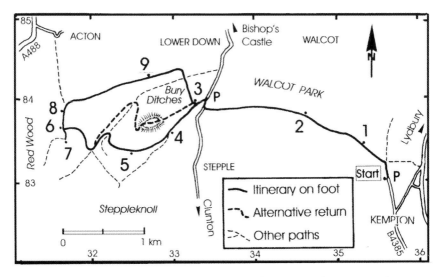

Figure 36. Kempton and Bury Ditches; Localities 1 to 9.

Overall the walking distance is 8km from start back to start. This can be shortened to 5km by returning to the start after locality 1 and moving any vehicle via Clunton to the Bury Ditches car park at SO334839 just before locality 3. The walking is mainly on well-made tracks usually dry and mud free. Bury Ditches is a spectacular hill fort which can be traversed on the return to either parking point. The route lies wholly on the 1:25000 OS Pathfinder sheet 930 for Bishop's Castle & Clun and the Explorer sheet 216. The geology is covered by the 1:50000 Montgomery sheet number 165.

From the start at Kempton walk through the Walcot entrance gates and after 150m bear left taking the track carrying the Shropshire Way heading NW with a stream on the left. In 400m the large quarry known as Sheepcote opens up on the right hand side (locality 1). Here, at near valley level, the rock is that of the Bailey Hill Formation, but higher in the sequence than seen in the vicinity of Edgton. Dipping to the SW it presents an alternating sequence of grey siltstones and fine sandstones with some levels showing millimetre scale laminations. Whilst undoubtedly deposited by waning currents these alternations appear as attenuated event-couplets, which so characterise the formation especially further west, and result either from storm generated currents or basinal turbidity flows (Cave *et al.* 1993, p. 101).

The main interest lies in the several levels of slumped bedding, typically 2 to 3 metres thick. On the left wall (west) there is a 2 metre zone of slumps which are seen to have a conglomeratic base some 10 to 15 cm thick. Above is a distinctive vertically jointed fine sandstone and, a little higher, a stepped bedding surface is overlain by a 0.5 metre slumped bed. Traced to the right this feature is lost in a further zone of disturbed bedding but the jointed sandstone reappears in the central portion of the quarry. On the right wall is a zone of flaggy but fragmented bedding cut by a 3 metre section of slumps with well formed "pillows" and succeeded by more massive and but slightly disturbed beds. Accumulation of these sediments on the slope of the outer shelf and their subsequent slippage triggered by tectonic movements immediately preceded the onset of the quieter deep water environment of the Knucklas Castle Formation.

The sediments in the quarry are generally unfossiliferous. Small distorted lenses of shelly material can be found and commonly these include broken tests of *Kirkidium knighti*. Sparse trilobite pygidia and the occasional brachiopod have also been found.

Continue along the track noting, in 700m, a second quarry, locality 2, opposite Lodge Farm. Although much obscured by vegetation this quarry exposes a further slumped horizon, but relationships are confused by two fault zones. These contain vertical strata and have caused much steepening of the dip of adjacent strata by the process of fault drag. The faults appear to be normal and downthrow is to the right.

In a further 400m a small excavation on the right with patches of shaly bedding marks a transition in the succession towards a deep water regime,which will have been completed by the next locality. Just after this the track makes a three-way split. Take the left-most branch, which descends slightly and passes through a gate to arrive at Stanley Cottage. 400m beyond this a tarmac road is reached. Here, turn right and after 100m turn left into the Forest Enterprise car park for Bury Ditches. Leave here by the track heading SW, waymarked in red for mountain bikes, noting the exposure on the right behind the pole barrier (locality 3).

This is the beginning of a complete and continuous outcrop of the Knucklas Castle Formation. Thinly bedded olive siltstones and mudstones contrast with those previously seen in the Bailey Hill Formation. Bedding is shaly down to a one millimetre spacing. Dip is low to the NW and the section continues as an embankment on the north side of the track for 600m to the small quarry of locality 4.

The uninterrupted section illustrates the nature of Knucklas Castle Beds, which are interpreted as of moderately deep sea origin (hemipelagites). The finely laminated layers contain carbonaceous material suggesting gentle current action by bottom currents possibly caused by distal turbidity flows. The mudstone component may well have accumulated from suspension fall-out.

The lithology suggests the possibility of graptolites, but none have been found. This implies that bottom waters were sufficiently oxygenated to bring about the breakdown of any organic remains. Low oxygen levels could support burrowing animals bringing about a mild degree of bioturbation. Thus, prolonged searching may reveal the odd burrow or worm track plus a pelagic fauna of small orthocones, ostracods and indeterminate bivalves. Casts of the brachiopod *Dayia navicula* occur and this species is probably indigenous. A feature of the beds is the sporadic development of highly calcareous nodules or concretions and this exposure shows an example as a metre-sized block broken by the prevalent jointing.

Continue along the main track as it curves round to run more directly east-west noting a gradual alteration in the lithology. The finely laminated bedding gives way to units with slightly undulose flaggy bedding on a 1 to 3cm scale. Over a distance of about 200m these units become thicker and more dominant until at a second quarry, locality 5, the shaly lithology is totally replaced and the beds are now those of the Cefn Einon Formation. Fossils, hitherto rare, also begin to appear, initially sparse and distributed within the rock matrix. The fauna comprises small brachiopods and bivalves. First appearances are usually of the strongly ribbed *Microsphaeridorhynchus* (prev. *Camarotoechia*) *nucula* and the smooth shelled bivalve *Fuchsella amygdalina*.

The change in lithology is undoubtedly due to decreasing water depth at the start of a major marine regression. The sediment, whilst still of silt grade, is coarser and bioturbation is more prominent partially destroying sedimentary detail. The fauna shows evidence of reworking indicating a more energetic current-swept environment.

The embankment section continues westwards for a further 350m ending abruptly just short of a hairpin bend. It is noticeable that individual rock units become generally thicker and massive typically reaching a 10cm thickness and begin to show, in spite of bioturbation, delicate cross-lamination indicative of the effect of water currents in a shallow environment. Fossils, mainly brachiopods characteristic of the Ludlovian Whitcliffe Stage, now occur plentifully sometimes scattered in clusters on bedding planes as well as within the rock matrix. The particular trio *Microsphaeridorhynchus nucula*, *Protochonetes ludloviensis* (look for attachment spines indicating an in life position) and *Salopina lunata* are principal members of a fossil association or community (Calef & Hancock, 1974; Watkins

1979; Lawson, 1994), which has a low diversity but high density aspect common in Whitcliffe age strata. The pale yellow colour of the decalcified siltstones corresponds exactly to the Llan Wen Hill Member (Figure 32), the type section for which is east of Knighton at SO307702.

From the hairpin continue along the main track for some 200m arriving, after a small ascent, in an open area between trees where there is an offset crossroads and a fifth track entering diagonally from the right. Turn right at the crossroads, heading northwest along a wide track, and after 250m branch left onto a narrower footpath which begins to descend through open woodland. Pieces of coarse micaceous sandstone lie in and alongside this path. This is Downton Castle Sandstone and there is a small working among the trees to the left shortly before the path encounters some steps, which descend to a wide forest road. This is locality 6 at the base of the Clun Forest Formation the marker for which are horizons of the densely packed gastropod *Turbocheilus* (previously *Platyschisma*) *helicites* and the bivalve *Modiolopsis complanata*. The vertical rock section alongside the steps usually shows at least one such horizon recognised by the deep rich brown colour of a decalcified rottenstone in which prolific casts of the above will be found. Other rottenstones should be found in rocky banks to left or right of the foot of the steps. The two marker fossils are usually taken to indicate brackish water conditions so it is of interest to examine the strata below and above this horizon.

Facing away from the steps walk to the left (southwards) along an ascending sequence. Outcrops of grey calcareous siltstone in places approach a limestone in composition and represent the *Platyschisma* Shale Member. Examples of *Turbocheilus helicites* and *Modiolopsis complananta* should be found and one or more bands of finely comminuted shell debris, perhaps with fish fragments. Continuing past an overgrown section the next outcrop is a sizeable excavation in the Downton Castle Sandstone Member (locality 7).

Coarse grained and rather "dirty" this sandstone is decidedly micaceous. Massively bedded it here lacks the clean yellow colour, current bedding and brachiopod *Lingula minima* found in outcrops of the type area located on the mid-shelf around Ludlow. However, it does contain plentiful plant remains recognised as short carbonaceous stem fragments usually assigned to *Cooksonia*.

Return to the steps and continue northwards. Vegetation is beginning to obscure this section (locality 8) and a degree of perseverance is needed to push through the colonising pine trees. Two features are of particular interest. Firstly, the shelf sediments deposited during the marine regression at the close of Ludlovian times were diachronous. The sediments deposited on the inner and mid-shelf areas show a physical transformation from marine through brackish to fluviatile conditions earlier than those deposited on the outer shelf edge. The type section at Ludford Corner in Ludlow defines the transformation as the Ludlow/Pridoli boundary. A good reliable zone fossil is required for which the only candidate currently appears to be the ostracod *Frostiella groenvalliana* whose appearance can be taken to mark precisely the base of the Pridoli Series. However, this ostracod was not found at locality 8 in a recent study by Miller (1995). 30m beyond the steps a section has been cleared (in summer 2000). Previously this had yielded examples of "bone bed" and fish fragments including an acathodian spine. The lithology is now more obvious being almost turbiditic in appearance indicating deposition by intermittent waning currents. Slightly micaceous bedding planes show scattered casts of *Turbocheilus helicites* and *Modiolopsis complanata* but also a quite high density of 1 to 2 millimetre sized ostracods. The state of preservation makes identification of the latter difficult in the field but they seem to include *Londinia fissurata*, which is consistent with this horizon. The presence of *Frostiella groenvalliana* is not yet proven!

Secondly, the regression is marked at locality 8 by sediments deposited in shallow offshore waters affected by wave action, tidal currents and current surges generated by storm events. It is one of the most dynamic environments in which sedimentary rocks form.

Immediately past the cleared section is a corner after which there is a 200m long section heading due north. The sediments display magnificently deposition in a very energetic environment. Dip is to the southeast, though the sloping bank limits any development of a deep vertical section. It would be difficult to produce a stratigraphic log that could consistently describe the whole section, which comprises an estimated 30 metres thickness of sediment.

The features exhibited are dominated by deposition from waning currents, with ripples on various scales from centimetre to metre. Notable are textbook examples of fossil lag deposits where equal sized shells, *Microsphaeridorhynchus nucula* and *Salopina lunata*, have accumulated in the hollows between ripple crests. Individual sedimentary units can be graded with bases deeply scored by sole marks. In other places the actions of burrowers can be seen with worm tracks and burrows. Fossils are largely confined to coquinas, such as the lag deposits mentioned above, but also much more diverse allogenic assemblages occur swept in by strong currents. Some sediments were laid down under less dynamic conditions, as towards the north end of the section, where there are scattered examples of the small brachiopod *Howellella elegans*. Here, a coquina yielded an abundance of this brachiopod together with trilobite pygidia and head shields (cephalons) of *Acastella spinosa*, the turreted gastropod *Loxonema* sp. (or *Holopella* sp.) and the ostracod *Calcibeyrichia torosa*.

This effectively completes the itinerary apart from a choice of return route to the Bury Ditches car park or Kempton. Two alternatives are suggested, either via the hill fort or a shorter way, which takes in a further locality.

For the hill fort return from the steps to the offset crossroads (between localities 5 and 6) and take the fifth diagonal path mentioned previously. This climbs steadily towards the fort at the approach to which it is necessary to do a long dog-leg to the right to gain an access stile. Beyond the stile the way is obvious. The fort was deliberately cleared of trees to reveal its extent and multi-ditch structure and now provides a splendid viewpoint.

For the shorter route continue round the right hand corner at the north end of locality 8. The forest road now continues on a ENE heading for 1.5km. The first kilometre provides a section, which reverses the sequence of Cefn Einon beds the base of which was seen at locality 5. The section ends at a quarry (locality 9), which is similarly at the same horizon. However, the larger vertical faces give a better impression of what is the Wern Quarry Member and particularly well illustrated is the effect of bioturbation. To quote from a description of the type section southwest of Knighton (Woodcock & Tyler, 1993, p.226) "...original lamination has been destroyed mainly by intense bioturbation. Only wispy remnants of lamination remain, together with the occasional thin continuous calcareous siltstone beds displaying parallel- or weak cross lamination."

A further 500m along and the forest road ends at a pair of impressive stone gate posts. From here it is but 200m ESE along the edge of the wood to reach a stile on the Shropshire Way and a further 400m SSE to reach the Bury Ditches car park.

ITINERARY 8

THE WREKIN AREA

Introduction

This whaleback hill (Figure 37) is probably the best known of the Shropshire Hills and is a familiar feature to travellers on the M54. Comprising volcanic rocks of the Precambrian basement it is the type area for the Uriconian. Aligned NE to SW it is defined on its northwest flank by the Wrekin Fault which downthrows Trias sandstones; in contrast on the southeast the volcanics are overlain unconformably by Cambrian strata followed by Ordovician and Lower Carboniferous.

Itinerary

The itinerary will examine both the volcanics and the later sedimentary cover. The circular route is followed using public rights of way, is approximately 11km long and involves one climb of 250m to the Wrekin summit. Two geological maps are published by BGS, the 1:50000 Shrewsbury Sheet 152 and the newer 1:25000 Telford

Figure 37. View looking northwards from Sheinton to The Wrekin, about 4km away and showing its whaleback profile, with the smaller Little or Primrose Hill to the left. In the foreground is the locally narrowed flood plain of the River Severn, with the tree-covered ridge of basal Silurian Kenley Grit on the far side. Beyond is the locally attenuated Cambrian and Ordovician sequence resting on the lower slopes of The Wrekin.

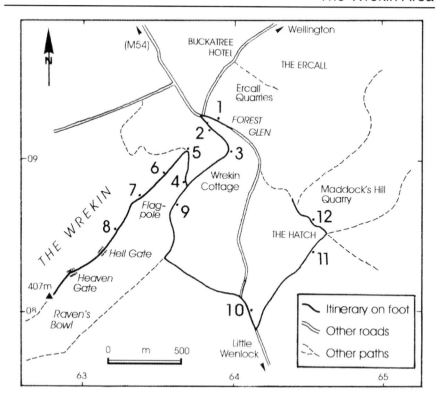

Figure 38. The Wrekin area; localities 1 to 12.

"Classic Areas" sheet. Memoirs are available for both maps. That for the Telford sheet (Hamblin & Coppack, 1995) gives a rather summary treatment whilst the Shrewsbury Memoir (Pocock, Whitehead et al. 1938) has much more detail, but copies are harder to find. The area is covered by the OS 1:25000 Explorer Telford map, number 242.

Lawrence's Hill Quarry (Start & Finish)

Parking is available at the Forest Glen car park, SJ639092, and can be easily reached from the M54, Wellington or Little Wenlock (Figure 38). Behind the car park is a disused quarry (locality 1) where good exposures of Precambrian Uriconian tuffs and agglomerates can be seen. It consists of two embayments separated by three near vertical NE/SW trending dolerite dykes, which appear to follow faults. The middle dyke is most easily examined and forms a prominent rib; there is much evidence of slickensided and brecciated material. The contact with the surrounding pyroclastic rocks is visible. The main face (61m high) is made up of layers of tuffs and agglomerates with inter-bedded lavas, which are seen to dip approximately north at an angle of 45 degrees. Figure 39 shows the succession of lavas and tuffs as recorded in the Shrewsbury memoir (Pocock, Whitehead *et al.*, 1938, page 17).

The Wrekin track

Cross the road and begin to climb the main track up the Wrekin. Some 100m on the right at the start of locality 2 are small exposures of vitric crystal tuffs showing banding and a little further on fine purple "flinty-looking" tuffs can be seen. Before a sharp right-hand bend there is an exposure, 3 metres high, of slightly coarser tuffs criss-crossed by joints. The basic dykes plotted on the geological maps are not clearly visible hereabouts because of vegetation and extra grit on the path.

As the track turns right (locality 3) a small exposure of unconformable Wrekin Quartzite (Cambrian) can be seen. and a change of colour in the rocks underfoot also indicates the presence of quartzite. The next section of the track is on quartzite and a bedding plane showing the southeast dip of the basal Cambrian can be examined on the right and in crags a few metres to the left of the path at the next sharp bend.

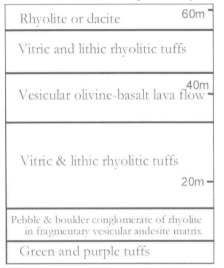

At this right-hand turn and just before the Wrekin Cottage on the right above there is a return to Uriconian rhyolites and tuffs (locality 4) which are visible in the path but not as large exposures. 50m from the bend a pebbly tuff is exposed as a band, on and parallel to the path. Continue past Wrekin Cottage taking the longer loop of the track as it swings southwest where there are more exposures of brecciated, vitric and crystalline tuffs (locality 5). Follow the track as it climbs towards the summit.

Figure 39. Forest Glen Quarry succession. Height above base in metres is shown.

Several more Uriconian outcrops and rock types can be examined and numerous dark dolerite dykes cross it. Some 200m from (5), and just before a firing range danger sign, a slightly raised exposure of coarser rhyolitic tuff (locality 6) can be examined on the left of the path. A few metres further on the distinctive dark rock of a dolerite dyke coincides with a bare roundish area also on the left but crossing the path. Another similar dyke is clearly seen just before reaching the first flagpole (locality 7).

At the flagpole and for some 40m beyond there is an interesting succession of changes in rock type involving a succession of grey tuffs, rhyolite, purple green tuffs and dolerite. The surface of the track to the summit becomes increasingly pink as it passes over more rhyolite. Between the second flagpole and "Hell Gate" (locality 8), especially near the danger board here, close examination of the rhyolite reveals small quartz veins, spherulitic textures and flow banding. There is some variation in the colour of the rhyolite from pale pink to a deeper brownish pink.

Passing Hell and Heaven Gates distinctive pink crags of flow-banded rhyolite are seen. Some of the exposures show evidence of auto-brecciation and rocks consist of succession of flows, which appear to have a northward dip at about 45 degrees. The thickness of the rhyolite flows seems to be around 600m and within them are a few signs of pyroclastic material. The rhyolites are hard compact rocks breaking with a splintery fracture. They represent several episodes of flow of viscous silica-rich lavas before increasing explosivity resulted in the eruption of pyroclastic material (ash, lapilli and volcanic bombs) which lithified to become tuffs and agglomerates as seen earlier.

It is worth pausing at the summit (on a clear day) to admire the extensive views. To the southwest the line of similar Uriconian whaleback hills, The Lawley, Caer Caradoc and Ragleth, mark the line of the Church Stretton Fault System. To the northeast this same system defines the Ercall and becomes the boundary fault to the Telford Coalfield. To the north and northwest the plain is relieved by a line of Triassic sandstone hills, Nesscliffe, Grinshill and Hawkstone. Nearer at hand to the southeast are the scarps of the sedimentary succession to be visited next.

Return along the ridge descending to Wrekin Cottage. As the track bends left at locality 4 bear to the right continuing along the path, which contours southwest. Along here a narrow band of Wrekin Quartzite separates the Uriconian to the right from the Cambrian Comley Sandstone in the valley to the left. Exposures are difficult to find but just up the slopes from a muddy brook one can find green-brown micaceous siltstone in the path (locality 9) belonging to the Comley Sandstone Formation. This same point can be reached from the summit by a very steep and rocky descent, not marked on the map of Figure 38, through Raven's Bowl to gain the same contour path.

Little Wenlock Basalt

Continue southwest from locality 9 for a distance of about 500m to take the footpath on the left (stile) which descends to cross the Shineton Shales of the valley and the unconformable junction between this Tremadocian and the Lower Carboniferous Lydebrook Sandstone and succeeding Carboniferous Limestone. At the road turn right and a few metres further on are weathered exposures of the Little Wenlock Basalt (locality 10). This is an amygdaloidal olivine lava flow within the lower part of the Carboniferous Limestone.

Carboniferous Limestone

Continue along the road to a plateau area where there is a footpath on the left. There are again magnificent views of the Wrekin, The Lawley and Caradoc, with Longmynd behind, and of the Clee Hills to the southeast. Take the footpath which heads northeast. It follows the strike of an outcrop of Carboniferous Limestone through woodland. This formation is very different from its equivalent in the Pennines and Derbyshire Peak being much more restricted in both thickness and outcrop. Here, it consists of grey, rubbly or massive limestones and micaceous shales, mudstones and yellow-brown friable calcareous sandstones, the latter easily confused with the underlying Lydebrook Sandstone. It is possible to leave the path and examine exposures of the grey-brown rubbly limestones in overgrown disused quarries where typical D2 sub-zone fossils, especially *Gigantoproductus* sp., can be found.

After a kilometre the path meets a track at a crossing by the derelict buildings of The Hatch. Some 150m before this on the right in the trees a good exposure of the sandy Carboniferous Limestone can be examined (locality 11). It is a striking yellow-brown with visible lamination. Continue to The Hatch. Extensive quarrying and mining of the limestone in the past extended into Limekiln Wood but has left very dangerous ground where exploration is not recommended.

Maddock's Hill

At the crossing proceed left downhill. The relationship between landscape features and rock types already seen can be appreciated in the view to the left where the unconformable boundary between the Lower Palaeozoic and younger strata is reflected in the terrain. Immediately right over a screening embankment is the now disused Maddock's Hill Quarry (locality 12). Here is one of the several lamprophyre intrusions emplaced within Cambrian and Lower Ordovician sedimentary rocks of the Midlands, notably at Nuneaton and at this locality. It takes the form of a lenticular mass intruded into the Tremadoc Shineton Shales and is a variety known as camptonite. Recent petrological and chemical data deduces that such sills are derived from hydrous, alkali-rich basic magmas formed and emplaced within regions of Ordovician compression, in this case around the northern margins of a stable Midlands massif (Thorpe, Gaskarth & Henney, 1993). In the field convincing evidence of compression can be seen in the folded near-vertical nature of the hardened shales in the southwest corner of the quarry. The 85 degree southeast dip contrasts strongly with much gentler dips in the opposite faces. Low grade metamorphic changes can be seen in the shales, which become indurated and spotted, as seen in small exposures along a footpath entering the quarry from the north. Yet the dendroid graptolite *Dictyonema flabelliforme* is hardly affected and can be found at some horizons. Weathered iron pyrite is common as discrete irregular crystals in the hardened shale, especially at the southwest end of the quarry.

The lamprophyre intrusion outcrops for approximately 0.8km in a NE/SW direction, this trend being reflected in the elongate shape of the quarry. Only the edges of the intrusion remain after working ceased on completion of the M54 in the early 1980's. There is much variation in crystal size (0.25 to 1.0mm.) and proportion of matrix, plagioclase and phenocrysts so that a range of interesting textures can be examined, but the mineralogy is complicated by alteration of the plagioclase, carbonate replacement of phenocrysts and chlorite replacement of interstitial pyroxene. Perhaps the two most striking textural characteristics readily visible are of clusters of mafic minerals in the darker rock and beautiful interlocking laths of oligoclase in the redder rock type. There is complex chemical variation within the sill. In the northwest of the quarry, i.e. the "bottom" of the sill, the rock is enriched in ferromagnesian minerals and is thus darker in colour compared with that in the southeast. This reflects some mineral redistribution by flowage differentiation. Chemical analysis, however, points to multiple intrusion of mafic magma into the lower part of a more felsic sill.

Other features of interest seen here are the faults and shatter zone in the camptonite with distinct calcite mineralization on the south face and an exposed unconformable boundary at the base of the Carboniferous Lydebrook Sandstone. This is visible at the top of the exposed face at the north eastern end of the quarry on the right. The sandstone is yellow in colour and fragments of this easily "stand out" in the scree below.

Continue down the track to meet the road, turn right and so return to the Forest Glen car park. If time allows a visit can be made to the Ercall Quarries, which are described in another G.A. publication (Toghill & Beale, 1994).

ITINERARY 9

CLEE HILLS

Preface

This area displays Lower Devonian to Upper Carboniferous strata that have been subject to gentle folding and which exhibit several unconformities reflecting late Caledonian (Acadian) and early Variscan earth movements. A dolerite sill of late Westphalian age, and actively quarried today, intrudes Lower and Middle Coal Measures of Titterstone Clee Hill.

The Clee Hills are an undulating hilly area in southeast Shropshire that lies between Bridgnorth and Ludlow. The B4364 Ludlow to Bridgnorth road traverses the area and the A4117 Ludlow to Kidderminster road skirts the south side of Titterstone Clee Hill. Brown Clee Hill (546m O.D.) and Titterstone Clee (533m O.D., with radiomasts and dolerite quarry) form very distinctive landmarks that afford excellent views of the West Midlands and Welsh Borderlands.

The localities described are scattered and mainly linked by narrow minor roads, so motor transport no larger than a small minibus, is essential, as are OS Explorer Sheets 203 (Ludlow) and 217 (The Longmynd and Wenlock Edge) 1:25000. British Geological Survey maps, 1:50,000, nos. 181 (Ludlow Sheet) and 166 (Church Stretton Sheet) are a valuable aid.

Some localities are roadside or adjacent to tracks and visitors should avoid hazardous parking. Loose rock material should not be left scattered on roads and tracks, and hammering is actively discouraged. The Countryside Code should be adhered to at all times with special care paid during the lambing and nesting seasons.

Introduction

The Lower Devonian to Upper Carboniferous strata (Figure 40) of the Clee Hills provide evidence of a range of sedimentary environments, while unconformities, faults and gentle folds represent phases of Acadian and early Variscan earth movements. This itinerary commences at the Bishop's Frome (Psammosteus) Limestone Member, which is taken as the base of the Devonian succession in the Welsh Borderland, with the under-lying Pridoli Series forming the highest division of the Silurian. The Devonian (or Old Red Sandstone) strata of the Clee Hills area represent a phase of continental sedimentation depositing fresh water limestones, mudstones, sandstones and conglomerates, that succeed conformably the predominantly shallow marine Silurian strata .

The Pridoli Series follows the final shallowing and closure of the Iapetus Ocean prior to the development of the Caledonian Mountains in this part of Britain. Late Caledonian or Acadian tectonism influenced sedimentation so that Middle Devonian strata are absent and the Upper Devonian Farlow Sandstone rests unconformably upon folded Lower Devonian Clee Formation sandstones.

Early Variscan earth movements had a marked influence on deposition such that

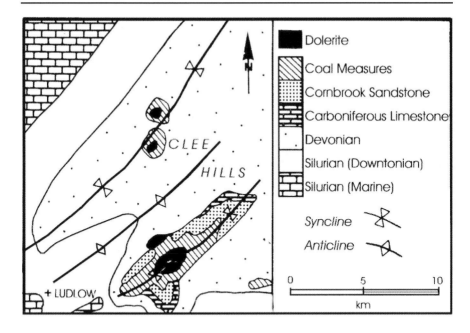

Figure 40.   Geological map of the Clee Hills.

early Carboniferous times saw a northward marine transgression from the south Britain region. Titterstone Clee Hill displays the northern 'feather-edge' of the transgression with a Carboniferous Limestone sequence resting unconformably on gently folded Devonian strata.   Further earth movements resulted in the Devonian strata and Carboniferous Limestone being overlain unconformably by the Namurian Cornbrook Sandstone Formation, which in turn displays an unconformable contact with an attenuated over-lying Coal Measures sequence.   The Carboniferous Limestone and Cornbrook Sandstone Formation are restricted to the area of Titterstone Clee Hill, being overstepped further north at Brown Clee Hill by Coal Measures which rest unconformably on Lower Devonian strata.   The Coal Measures have been intruded by an olivine-dolerite sill up to 90m thick of (late) Westphalian D age.   The dolerite is known locally as 'dhustone'.

Devonian

A minor road cutting (SO 585898) between Shipton and Ditton Priors displays a section through the Bishop's Frome (Psammosteus) Limestone Member.   This locality is reached by turning west off the B4364 Bridgnorth to Ludlow road at Cleobury North, or turning southeast from the B4368 Craven Arms to Bridgnorth road at Shipton.   Parking is recommended at a wide field gate entrance 250m southeast of this steep, narrow road section. This moderately resistant limestone dips gently eastwards and forms a low, but distinctive scarp feature that can be traced along the western flank of the Clee Hills. The limestone is pale, fine-grained, and conglomeratic in places and can be employed as a stratigraphic marker horizon. The name 'Cornstone' is often applied to this limestone, which is believed to have formed by soil producing processes during periods of desiccation, leading to the chemical precipitation of calcium carbonate. If the *in-situ* cornstone is then reworked as a consequence of the scouring activities caused by an influx of fast flowing water, perhaps flash -floods, then the result is a conglomeratic cornstone.

From the Bishop's Frome Limestone section drive 2km eastwards to Ditton Priors, and then turn southwest on a minor road towards Abdon (SO 575863) on the west side of Brown Clee Hill. At Abdon continue southwards. and 1km north of Clee St Margaret turn left at the crossroads towards Cockshutford. After 200m there is a roadside car park (SO 572851). From here walk towards the Nordey Bank hill fort. Dittonian (Lower Devonian) sandstones form two small, west-facing exposures on the upper part of the earthworks. The larger of the two shows one metre of very coarse-grained red sandstones overlying 72cm of coarse grained green sandstones. The red sandstone shows a poor degree of sorting, and includes matrix-supported shale clasts up to 1.5cm long that tend to be orientated parallel to and concentrated on lamination surfaces. This sandstone is feldspathic and displays greenish-grey reduction patches. The green sandstone tends to oxidise to a reddish colour on exposure to the atmosphere. This rock is better sorted, and quartzo-feldspathic with no shale clasts

From Nordey Bank there are good views westwards across the dip slopes of the Silurian escarpments including Wenlock Edge to the Stretton Hills.

Dolerite

Leaving Nordey Bank drive south through Stoke St Milborough and turn right (southwestwards) onto the B4364. After 5km turn left (east) onto the A4117 towards Kidderminster. An alternative route on minor roads can be tried via Bitterley, which crosses a section of the Titterstone Clee/Bitterley Incline, part of the railway once used for transporting quarried dolerite to Ludlow for distribution. The A4117 rises onto and along the south side of Clee Hill. Just after Angelbank (SO 575759) look for the minor road to Dhustone which becomes the access road to the radar installations on the Titterstone Clee summit. After 2.5km redundant dolerite quarries and workings under the summit provide good exposure of this black, fine-grained rock (Figure 41). On a clear day there are excellent views across South Shropshire, the West Midlands and into Wales where the relation of topography to geology can be very well appreciated. Return to the A4117. One kilometre east of Cleehill village on the A4117 park at the roadside (SO 602758) next to a small abandoned dolerite quarry at the top of Cornbrook Dingle (Figure 42).

The dolerite mass of Titterstone Clee is a sill, up to 90m thick, that has been extensively quarried as a source of road metal. The exposure here is of a fine-grained olivine-dolerite that displays columnar jointing.

Figure 41. The disused dhustone quarries of Titterstone Clee viewed from the south at a distance of about 1km. The thick basalt sill is intruded into Lower Coal Measures which occupy the foreground. Erosion has removed the measures above the sill.

Namurian Cornbrook Sandstone Formation

Cross the road and carefully walk down the dingle. The rough, steep path adjacent to the stream is frequently boulder strewn. There are several outcrops of the Cornbrook Sandstone Formation that dip in the range 45°-70° towards 335°. The thickly bedded yellowish sandstone is usually very coarse-grained with conglomeratic horizons and well developed graded bedding. Slickensided joint surfaces are common, suggesting the possible proximity of a fault. Cross the very minor road and on the east bank of the stream are overgrown spoil tips, the result of smelting of the iron ore that was extracted from the local Coal Measures, a minor industry long abandoned. Return to the minor road and a short walk eastwards reveals views to the south and southeast. The continuation of the outcrop of the Cornbrook Sandstone produces higher, rougher ground in contrast to the Carboniferous Limestone and Devonian strata, which forms lower, better pasture. On the skyline are the Abberley and Malvern Hills, and beyond is the Cotswold escarpment.

Devonian and Carboniferous Limestone

From Cornbrook Dingle continue east on the A4117 and turn left at Foxwood (SO 621767) or Hopton Wafers (SO 636763) onto minor roads north to Farlow. Limited safe

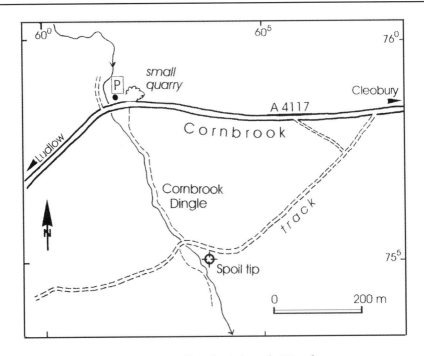

Figure 42. Cornbrook Dingle.

parking is available next to St Giles Church in the centre of Farlow (SO 639806). To start at the base of the local succession walk northeastwards for 200m down the steep hill until reaching a narrow road cutting (SO 641808) partly overhung by trees (Figure 43). In this cutting and at the base of an access track to an adjacent field gate Dittonian (Lower Devonian) strata dip at 19°/250° (locality 1). The rocks are brown mudstones and silt-stones, the latter sometimes grading into very fine-grained sandstones.

The sandstones are thinly bedded (4-6cm), micaceous and sometimes display pale greenish-grey reduction patches. The siltstones and very fine-grained sandstones exhibit cross bedding.

As a result of the Acadian (late Caledonian) earth movements Middle Devonian strata are absent in the Clee Hills area and Upper Devonian strata rest unconformably on the Lower Devonian. Retrace the route taken and the unconformity is crossed just before the sharp bend (Figure 43). Immediately beyond this bend, on both sides of the road, yellow Farlow Sandstones are exposed (locality 2). These range upwards from poorly sorted conglomeratic beds 1-2m thick to well sorted very fine to medium grained sandstones that are sometimes thinly bedded (5cm minimum). The conglomeratic sandstones contain distinctive white pebbles.

Beyond the next tight bend on the steepest part of this road section the Upper Devonian - Lower Carboniferous unconformity is crossed. The exact position of this unconformity is uncertain because it is suspected that the Carboniferous sequence may

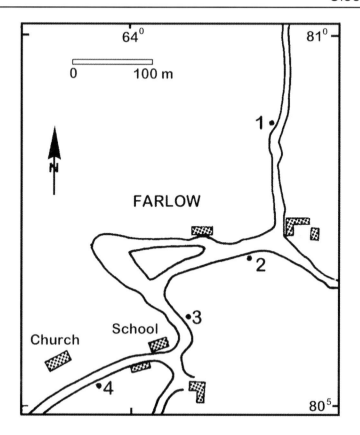

Figure 43. Farlow locality map.

have slipped and might not be in-situ. The younger Carboniferous strata are much more steeply inclined 70º/131º (locality 3) than the underlying Devonian, and a rotational slip could explain this apparent dip. Other instances of mass movement of the Carboniferous strata are known in this area. The following Carboniferous sequence is exposed:-

Oreton Limestone Formation	1m
Shaly limestone (Lower Limestone Shale Group)	1m
Basal Pebbly Sandstone	0.7m

The pebbly sandstone is poorly sorted; some pebbles are composed of reddish jasper. The shaly limestone splits into irregular layers up to 3cm thick. It is a medium-grained, pale grey limestone that is slightly oolitic, yields occasional crinoid ossicles and displays discrete calcite grains. The succeeding limestone is oolitic and yields a K-zone fauna, including bryozoa and quite large productids. These limestones also crop out just inside the field immediately south of the church (locality 4).

ITINERARY 10

BRIDGNORTH SANDSTONES:
Quatford to Worfe Bridge

Introduction

At the close of Carboniferous times a marine regression occurred. Desert conditions developed over the land and left a local record in beds of bright red sandstone forming a scarp facing the town of Bridgnorth from the east. This itinerary explores this scarp and adjacent exposures recognising features within the red sandstone which support its description as a "dune sandstone". The relationship to overlying conglomerates is also considered.

Only two formations are involved but, because of a new stratigraphical classification, these have a dual nomenclature (Toghill, 1990). The older regime identifies a Triassic Bunter Series of Lower Mottled (Dune) Sandstone succeeded by Bunter Pebble Beds; the newer gives a Permian Bridgnorth Sandstone overlain by the Kidderminster Conglomerate of the Triassic Sherwood Sandstone Group and clearly implies that this is a local type area for dune sandstones of the Permian.

Sand dunes are unequivocally transient structures and it can be difficult to accept their preservation in the sedimentary record - surely they would be washed away by the first marine inundation? A degree of scepticism is indeed justifiable and it is not always easy to recognise ancient wind deposited sediments, although it is accepted that they do form part of the geological record (Duff, 1993, chapter 22).

Ripples, sediment "waves" and dunes move downstream or down-wind by transport of lifted grains from a gently sloping "stoss side" to deposition by avalanching down a steeper "lee side". The oblique lamination produced by these mechanisms, as the foresets of the ripples, waves or dunes advance, is commonly referred to as cross-bedding. It may be argued that since avalanching produces chaotic deposits there should be no sign of cross bedding in sand dunes. A possible explanation is that avalanching grains behave something like a fluid - a fluidised bed would be an apt analogy - and when settling take up some degree of order by sorting processes.

As erosion is taking place at the same time as deposition it is necessary for preservation that there be net deposition of sediment. This is particularly the case with sand dunes where, of the great variety of forms that can be assumed, it is the large scale transverse variety which commonly becomes the major feature of net deposition when sand is abundant. When sand supply is limited for some reason smaller crescentic dunes, the barchans of popular desert imagery, move across bedrock surfaces (Karpeta, 1990).

Itinerary

The itinerary, Figure 44, is described as a linear walk of about 9km entirely on public footpaths and roads. It may be shortened by using a vehicle between localities 1 and 3, thus omitting (2) and saving 4km. Paths are in good condition and usually

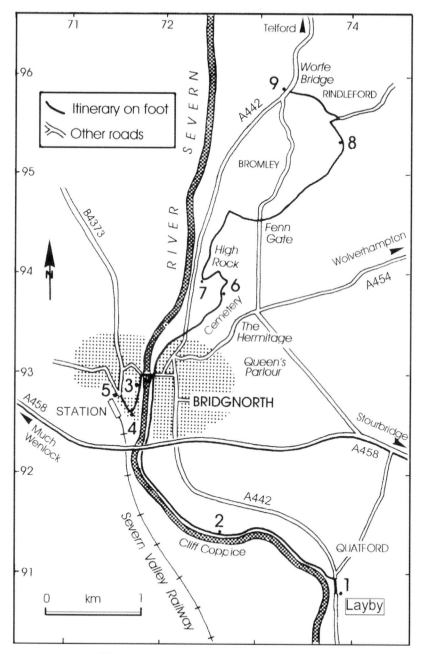

Figure 44. Quatford to Worfe Bridge; localities 1 to 9.

dry except for the river bank between (1) and (2). It may also be more convenient to use a car park at the cemetery (see below) instead of or in addition to any in Bridgnorth town.

Quatford

There is a large off-road lay-by at SO738904 just south of Quatford Church on the A442 Bridgnorth to Kidderminster road adjacent to locality 1, a section at the north end of the lay-by. It will pay to spend some time at this locality since it establishes several criteria for the rest of the excursion. Between the church and main road is an L-shaped section in red sandstone which gives an overall view of a planar cross-bedded unit. The "bedding" is almost fractal in that units on a 10 to 20cm scale are themselves lineated at the centimetre level and these in turn are crudely laminated down to a 1mm scale. Below 1mm are individual sand grains which a hand lens will show as exclusively quartz, well rounded, all roughly the same size and free of either a coarse fraction or fines. Insofar as equi-sized grains can produce an appearance of bedding careful examination of, say, 1cm units will show very slight variation in grain size, typically fining upwards, with a suggestion of parallel variation in the degree of cementation or at least hardness. However, it is also obvious that in parts the sandstone is now virtually uncemented since it is densely bored by some insect - possibly a species of wasp - and overall any cementation matrix is hard to find. The sandstone has a porosity to be expected of a deposit of close-packed grains and it is remarkable that such a rock will, nevertheless, sustain high vertical faces.

Moving towards the road note how the changed angle of dip around the L-shaped exposure gives a 3-dimensional perspective from which the true direction and magnitude of the dip of this cross-bedded unit can be calculated. At the pavement walk 20m north to a section cut by a road re-alignment. This major feature is a single trough-bedded unit exposed on both sides of the road so that its E-W orientation is clear. The curved bedding is seen to wedge out as it approaches the horizontal base, an effect described as tangential-bedding. Such a unit is to be viewed as the cross-section of a small crescentic or barchan dune moving from east to west. It is interpreted as running up the relatively flat stoss-side of a large transverse dune (Karpeta, 1990). As the most ephemeral of dune forms preservation may seem to be somewhat fortuitous were it not for rapid burial beneath other forms providing net deposition. The trough bed is embedded within a second unit and below the line of the old road surface are planar cross-beds of a possible transverse dune. Above, the trough is truncated by three different cross-beds. At the scale of the section these appear linear but traced to left or right are slightly curved or tangential.

Walk north down the hill by pavement or old road some 300m into the village. Opposite a bus-stop and telephone kiosk a footpath leads down to the river which is followed upstream for 1500m to locality 2.

River Terrace

The sharp wooded edge of Cliff Coppice on the opposite river bank is cut into Keele Beds of Upper Coal Measures age and marks the edge of the so-called Main Terrace of the River Severn. The flat top represents the height of the river channel at the time of the last ice-age since it is covered by fluvio-glacial deposits derived in part from the melting of Irish Sea Ice. This terrace can be traced upstream for 6km to Apley, where it merges with the flanks of Ironbridge Gorge, and downstream as far as Kidderminster.

Continue along the river bank for 2km where the path emerges in Bridgnorth Lower Town at the east abutment of the river bridge. Note the path's continuation on the opposite side of the road. Cross the bridge, bear left and continue to Castle Hill Gardens (locality 3) which starts 100m beyond the entrance to the Cliff Railway.

Bridgnorth Sandstone

In the cliffs behind these gardens the effect is one of scale, with several trough-bedded units interbedded above and below with planar cross-beds. The previous interpretation as westward migrating transverse dunes with superimposed barchan dunes still applies. The numerous caverns are the remains of excavated dwellings and one may still be accessible at the farther southern end where a 3-dimensional section can be examined. The gardens also provide a good view of the sandstone escarpment to the east of the river capped by fluviatile Kidderminster Conglomerate. From right to left the red quarry face of Queen's Parlour is topped by a white trig. point with the Hermitage in trees to the left and then, further away, High Rock of locality 7. Descend steps to the pavement and continue south. At the road fork go right up the hill for 50m to the corner of Castle Hill (locality 4). Here, an exposure has two features of interest. Firstly, it shows an example of steeply dipping foresets which approach a practical inclination limit of 34 degrees for aeolian sands (Duff, 1993, p. 485). Secondly, examination with a hand lens shows some layers with reverse grading, that is coarsening upward on a 1 centimetre scale. Reverse grading can result from the sieving and shaking effects when bundles of sand grains avalanche down lee slopes or when an increasing wind strength progressively winnows finer grains from an exposed sand surface.

Continue around the corner to Canon Steps, cross the road (care!) and follow more steps to the lower level then go right beneath the footbridge towards the Seven Valley Railway station and locality 5. As an illustration of cementation and/or diffusion phenomenon are thin convoluted upstanding bands of black iron-stained sandstone. These bands can occur along a straight bonding surface or cut across bedding lamination in a totally irregular way. Their origin would seem to relate to some solution and/or diffusion effect, possibly when the sands were near a water table.

Return and cross the river bridge, take the footpath northward on the east bank of the river for 500m, then turn right across Severn Park to the main road. Cross over to reach the entrance to the cemetery at SO724935. Vehicles may be parked here. Climb steps leading north, follow the path around the upper edge of the cemetery and continue uphill to a small cutting on the edge of trees (locality 6).

Kidderminster Conglomerate

Although in an overgrown area the path can be seen to cross from the now familiar dune sandstone to an irregularly bedded coarse sandstone with patches of conglomerate. This is the Kidderminster Conglomerate capping the scarp seen from locality 3. There are several better exposures between here and the next location at High Rock, both alongside the path and on the hillside above, as at High Rock itself. The fluviatile origin of these beds is unmistakable. Only powerful water flow could move pebbles and cobbles of the size present. The sandstone has grains which are sharp, angular and of a size which grades from 1mm to the finest visible. It usually has a calcite cementation but this weathers out in surface exposures. The conglomerate can itself have a calcareous matrix when it becomes very hard but more usually this matrix is of sand. The clasts generally show varying degrees of wear from occasional angular pieces to well rounded cobbles albeit with surface damage marks. Size distribution seems bi-modal and the conglomerate would be classed as matrix supported since the larger pebbles are not in contact. The provenance of these pebbles has been much studied and, as can be seen, several mono-mineralic hard rocks are present, viz. quartzite, chert, sandstone and limestone, but rarely such multi-mineral rocks as granite and gneiss. These latter may, however, be the source of discrete heavy mineral grains which can be separated from the sandy matrix.

High Rock

From the cutting turn left and fork left again at a waymarked post to pass down a ramp and round the head of a small valley. Here are several exposures of conglomerate and the path then emerges at the spectacular viewpoint of High Rock (locality 7). Scattered trees and natural crags surround this local beauty spot with a splendid southerly view down the Severn valley. Many bedding planes are exposed giving opportunity to the talents of the local graffiti artists. The dune sandstone drops sheer to the road but it is possible to descend the slope to the south and examine quarried sections below.

The path continues northwards through woods; keeping near to the top of the scarp it emerges with a sharp right turn into an overgrown lane which leads down to a road at Fenn gate. Field paths then continue northeast into Batch Valley which joins the River Worfe just southeast of Rindleford.

Rindleford quarry

The abrupt appearance at locality 8 of the long monolithic faces of this quarry is unexpected. However, it neatly encapsulates interpretation of some of those criteria which distinguish between aeolian and fluvial sandstones. The faces of apparently uniform sandstone display just those features of cross, tangential and even hummocky stratification which might suggest aeolian sands. These are, however, fluviatile features; "dip" angles are low, there are flat horizontal bonding surfaces, the sandstone is sharp coarse grained with, critically, a scattering of small pebbles. The quarry exploited a large coherent bed of nearly pure sandstone within the Kidderminster Conglomerate unit.

Proceed past the quarry, over a footbridge, past a mill to the road where turn left and follow for 800m to the junction with the main A442.

Worfe Bridge

Bearing in mind earlier points that preservation of fragile dune sandstone structures seems problematic then the sections at locality 9 show how this could take place. A considerable thickness of interbedded dunes had accumulated; a change of regime brought fluviatile conditions and rivers and/or flash floods began to cascade sand and pebbles over the dune landscape. The upper parts of the dune sands were repeatedly washed away creating a succession of erosion surfaces. On occasion current strength decreased to a level where rivers began to drop their bed load, cobbles and pebbles first. These immediately protected the erosion surface effectively sealing it from further erosion and thereafter the mixed facies of conglomerate and fluviatile sandstones accumulated.

On the west side of the road, north of the bridge, a cut section shows cross-bedded dune sandstones with the undulating erosion surface dipping gently to the northeast. This is succeeded by a 1 metre thickness of conglomerate with clasts up to cobble size which fills hollows in the erosion surface. Beds above are intermingled coarse pebbly cross-bedded sandstones and conglomerate lenses. The same features occur to the south of the bridge on the east side of the road. Here, the conglomerate itself is truncated by a major flat parting with an erosion surface dipping 5 degrees north cutting through this basal surface. This section is followed to the south by over 100m of interleaved cross, tangential and trough-bedded sandstones.

To return to the cemetery car park, Bridgnorth town or the start, whilst avoiding the main road, take the lane opposite signposted "Bromley". This leads in 1km to Fenn Gate from where the outward route may easily be retraced.

FURTHER READING

ALLENDER, R. et al. 1960. Summer Field Meeting at Ludlow. *Proc. Geol Assoc.,* **71**, 209-232.

BASSETT, M.G. 1989. The Wenlock series in the Wenlock area. In Bassett, M.G.& Holland; C.H. eds.(1989). *A Global Standard for the Silurian System.* Chapter 6, 51-73; National Museum of Wales, Geological Series No. 9, Cardiff.

CALEF, C.E. & HANCOCK, N.J. 1974. Wenlock and Ludlow marine communities in Wales and the Welsh Borderland. *Palaeontology,* **17**, 779-810.

CARNEY, J.N. *et al.* 2000. *Precambrian Rocks of England and Wales.* Geological Conservation review Series No. 20, Joint Nature Conservation Committee, Peterborough.

CAVE, R., HAINS, B.A. & WHITE, D.E. 1993. *The Wenlock and Ludlow of the Newtown area.* In Geological Excursions in Powys, No. 14 in National Museum of Wales Geological Series, chapter 3, 85-112.

COCKS, L.R.M. 1989. The geology of South Shropshire. *Proc. Geol. Assoc.,* **100**, 505-519.

COMPSTON, W., WRIGHT, A,E, & TOGHILL, P. 2002. Dating the Late Precambrian Volcanicity of England and Wales. *Journal of the Geological Society,* **159**, 323-339.

COPE, J.W. 2000. In *Precambrian Rocks of England and Wales.* Geological Conservation Review Series No. 20, Joint Nature Conservation Committee, Peterborough.

DUFF, P. McL. 1993. *Holmes' Principles of Physical Geology,* 4th Edition. Stanley Thornes, Cheltenham.

ELLES, G.L. & SLATER, B.A. 1906. The Highest Silurian Rocks of the Ludlow District. *Quarterly Journal Geological Society,* **62**, 195 -220.

FORTEY, R.A. & OWENS, R.M. 1992. The trilobite *Angelina* unstretched. *Geology Today,* November-December, 219-221.

GREIG D.C., WRIGHT J.E., HAINS B.B. & MITCHELL G.H. 1968. *Geology of the country around Church Stretton, Craven Arms, Wenlock Edge and Brown Clee.* BGS Memoir for Sheet 166.

HAMBLIN, R.J.O. & COPPACK, B.C., 1995. *Geology of Telford and the Coalbrookdale Coalfield.* BGS Memoir for the 1:25000 Telford Sheet SJ60 and parts SJ61, 70 & 71.

HOLLAND, C.H., LAWSON J.D. & WALMSLEY V.G. 1963. *The Silurian Rocks of the Ludlow district, Shropshire.* Bull. Brit. Museum (Geology), **8**, 95-171.

KARPETA, W.P. 1990. The morphology of Permian palaeodunes - a reinterpretation of the Bridgnorth Sandstone around Bridgnorth, England, in the light of modern dune studies. *Sedimentary Geology,* **69**, 59-75.

Further Reading

LAWSON, J.D. 1973. New Exposures on forestry roads near Ludlow. *Geological Journal*, **8**, 279-284.

_____, 1994. Review of UK Silurian associations. In J.Boucot & J.D.Lawson (eds.) *Palaeocommunities*, chapter 3.

_____, & WHITE, D.E. 1989. The Ludlow Series in the Ludlow area. In Bassett, M.G. & Holland, C.H. (eds.) (1989) *A Global Standard for the Silurian System*, chapter 7, 73 -90; National Museum of Wales, Geological Series No. 9, Cardiff.

LOYDELL, D.K. 1998. Early Silurian sea-level changes. *Geological Magazine*, **135**, 447-471.

LYNAS, B.D.T. 1988. Evidence for dextral oblique-slip faulting in the Shelve Ordovician Inlier, Welsh Borderland: implications for the south British Caledonides. *Geological Journal*, **23**, 39-57.

McNAMARA, K.J. 1978. Symbiosis between gastropods and bryozoans in the late Ordovician of Cumbria, England. *Lethaia*, **11**, 25-40.

MILLER, C.G. 1995. Ostracode & conodont distribution across the Ludlow/Pridoli boundary of Wales and the Welsh Borderland. *Palaeontology*, **38**, 341-348.

MOLYNEUX, S. 1999, The Ludlow Series (Upper Silurian) of the type area. In *The Ludlow Holostrat*, http://www.bgs.ac.uk, 1-90.

MOSELEY, J. 1992. A-level field-work guide: The Welsh Borderland. *Geology Today*, March-April, 66-70.

PATTRICK, R.A.D. & BOWELL, R.J. 1991. The genesis of the West Shropshire Orefield: evidence from fluid inclusions, sphalerite chemistry and sulphur isotopic ratios. *Geological Journal*, **6**, 101-115.

PAULEY, J.C. 1986. *The Longmyndian Supergroup: facies, stratigraphy and structure*. Unpublished Ph.D. thesis, University of Liverpool.

_____,1990. Sedimentary, structural evolution and tectonic setting of the late Precambrian Longmyndian Supergroup of the Welsh Borderland, UK. In D'lemos, R.S.Strachan & C.G. Topley (eds.) *The Cadomian Orogeny*, Geol. Soc. Spec. Publ. no. 51, 341-351.

_____, 1991. A revision of the stratigraphy of the Longmyndian Supergroup, Welsh Borderland, and of its relationship to the Uriconian volcanic complex. *Geological Journal*, **26**, 167-183.

PHARAOH, T.C., WEBB, P.C., THORPE, R,S, & BECKINSALE, R.D.,1987. Geochemical evidence for the tectonic setting of the late Proterozoic volcanic suites in central England. In Pharaoh,T.C., Beckinsale, R.D. & Rickard, D. (eds.) *Geochemistry and Mineralization of Proterozoic Volcanic suites*. Geological Society Special publication No. 33, 541-552.

POCOCK, R.W., WHITEHEAD, T.H. et al., 1938. *Shrewsbury District including the Hanwood Coalfield*. BGS Memoir for the 1:50000 Shrewsbury Sheet 152.

SALTER, J.W., 1856. On some fossil remains in the Cambrian rocks of the Longmynd and North Wales, *Quarterly Journal Geological Society*, **12**, 246-251.

_____, 1857. On Annelide-burrows and surface markings from the Cambrian rocks of the Longmynd. *Quarterly Journal Geological Society*, **13**, 199-206.

SIVETER, D.J., OWENS, R.M. & THOMAS, A.T. 1989. *Silurian Field Excursions; a geotraverse across Wales and the Welsh Borderland*. National Museum of Wales, Geological series No. 10, Cardiff.

THORPE, R.S., GASKARTH, P.J. & HENNEY, P.J., 1993. Composite Ordovician intrusions around the Midlands Micro-craton in Central Britain. *Geological Magazine*, **130**, 000-000.

TOGHILL, P, 1990. *Geology in Shropshire*. Swan Hill Press, Airlife Publishing, Shrewsbury.

_____, 1992. The Shelvian Event, a late Ordovician tectonic episode in southern Britain (Eastern Avalonia). *Proc. Geol. Assoc.*, **103**, 31-35.

_____, 2000. *Geology of Britain - An introduction*. Swan Hill Press, Airlife Publishing, Shrewsbury.

_____ & BEALE, S., 1994. *Ercall Quarries, Wrekin area, Shropshire*. Geology Teaching Trail, G.A. Guide no. 48, 1-21.

TUCKER, R.D. & PHARAOH, T.C. 1991. U-Pb zircon ages for late Precambrian igneous rocks in Southern Britain. *Journal Geological Society*, **148**, 435-443.

WATKINS, R. 1979. Benthic community organisation in the Ludlow Series of the Welsh Borderland. *Bull. Brit. Museum (Geology series)*, **31**, 175-280.

WHITE, D.E. & LAWSON, J.D. 1978. *The stratigraphy of new sections in the Ludlow Series of the type area, Ludlow, Salop, England*. Special Report 78/30 of the Institute of Geological Sciences, 1-10.

WHITAKER, J.H.McD. 1962. The geology of the area around Leintwardine, Herefordshire. *Quarterly Journal Geological Society*, **108**, 319-352.

_____. 1994. Silurian basin slope sedimentation and mass movement in the Wigmore Rolls area, central Welsh Borderland. *Journal Geological Society*, **151**, 27.

WHITTARD W.F. 1932; Stratigraphy of the Valentian Rocks of Shropshire. *Quarterly Journal Geological Society*, **88**, 859-902.

WILSON, D. 2000. In *Precambrian Rocks of England and Wales*. Geological Conservation Review Series no. 20, Joint Nature Conservation Committee, Peterborough.

WOODCOCK, N.H. 1984. The Pontesford Lineament, Welsh Borderland. *Journal Geological Society*, **141**, 1001-14.

_____ & FISCHER, M. 1986. Strike-slip duplexes. *Journal of Structural Geology*, **8**, 725-735.

_____ & TYLER, J.E., 1993. The Ludlow and Pridoli of the Radnor Forest to Knighton area. In *Geological Excursions in Powys*, No. 14. National Museum of Wales Geological Series, chapter 8, 209-228.

APPENDIX

SSSI's and RIGS

1. SITES OF SPECIAL SCIENTIFIC INTEREST (SSSI's)

Geological SSSI's have the same degree of legal protection accorded to the more common Biological SSSI's and, indeed, the two forms are sometimes combined. Their status is one of national importance and their designation or "notification" is accomplished at national level. Ensuring that the sites continue to exist lies within the remit of English Nature and in several cases a long term management plan may be funded to ensure proper conservation.

Below is given a list of those Geological SSSI's which are explicitly visited by the itineraries in this guide. The format of each of the 11 entries is as follows:

A numbered header gives the official name of the SSSI, its grid reference and an indication of the type of geological exposure(s). The following line(s) give the stratigraphy exhibited in terms of Period, Formation and age. There then follows a summarised extract from the "Description and Reasons for Notification" insofar as this is relevant to particular itinerary localities. The latter are indicated in brackets.

1. LONGMYND   (SO420950 - variously quarries, natural outcrops and crags)

The Longmynd SSSI (see Itinerary 1) forms the type locality for the Longmyndian succession of probable Precambrian age. All the type localities for the seven group subdivisions in Longmyndian stratigraphy are included.

Specifically noted is the Ashes Hollow Quarry (SO434930, locality 4) whose beds contain enigmatic impressions of possible medusoid origin and 'worm' trails. These show affinity with fossils described from late Precambrian strata in northern Russia. Also mentioned are the tuffaceous beds of the 'Batch Volcanics' of the Synalds Group seen at locality 10.

2. THE STIPERSTONES (SJ370000 various natural tors, boulder fields & quarries)

The Stiperstones SSSI (see Itinerary 4) covers the Stiperstones Quartzite ridge whose rock is of Ordovician Arenig age and a large area of ground to the west from Mytton Dingle to Bergam Quarry with many exposures of the underlying Mytton and Tankerville Flags.

The Stiperstones ridge is capped by a series of quartzite tors (localities 3a & 3b). The tors are surrounded by block fields of angular boulders with examples of stone circles which elongate downslope and merge into stone stripes which cover the flanks of the ridge. The tors, circles and stripes were formed under periglacial conditions probably during the last glaciation.

The Mytton Flags (locality 4) yield a rich trilobite fauna which includes species of the shallow water "Neseuretus community". At Bergam Quarry (locality 5a) are horizons containing an assemblage of trilobites known as a "raphiophorid community".

3. SHELVE CHURCH SECTION (SO337990 exposures below churchyard wall)
   Ordovician Mytton Flags of Arenig age.
   This famous (erstwhile) exposure of Mytton Flags (see Itinerary 4) contained a more prolific mix of graptolite, trilobite and brachiopod fauna than can be found at any comparable Shropshire site. It is now necessarily replaced by the remains of an excavation for a barn (SO335990).

4. SNAILBEACH MINE (SJ374023 disused mine and mine dumps)
   Ordovician Mytton Flags containing series of lead-barium mineral veins.
   Extensive mine dumps (see Itinerary 4) testify to the scale of working in the Snailbeach mine. The principal dump has now been "reclaimed" but a conservation section retains material from which specimens of galena, sphalerite, barite, calcite and witherite can be obtained.

5. HOPE VALLEY (SJ342015-357021 natural and quarried exposures)
   Ordovician Hope Shales of Llanvirn age and including the unconformable contact of the overlying Silurian Venus Bank Formation of Llandovery age.
   This is the type section for the Hope Shales (see Itinerary 4). Within the site are some of the richest faunas in the British Llanvirn series. A number of conodont species have been found.

6) MORTIMER FOREST (SO470730 exposures along forest roads)
   Silurian Ludlow Series
   The SSSI notifies numerous standard body and boundary stratotype sections for the Elton, Bringewood, Leintwardine and Whitcliffe Formations within the Ludlovian.
   The standard and other sections exposed along Goggin Road, Deer Park Road and Sunnyhill Track are wholly the subject matter of Itinerary 5. localities 1 to 11.

7. EATON TRACK (SO501900 track side and surface exposure)
   Silurian Wenlock Series
   This internationally important locality is a reference section for the Homerian Stage of the Silurian Period. The section (see Itinerary 6, locality 1) also spans a zonal junction defined by the changing make-up of graptolites. This junction is discernible world-wide and is of key importance in comparing rock sequences internationally.

8. HILLEND QUARRY (SO396876 quarry (and roadside) sections)
   Silurian Pentamerus Beds of Llandovery age.
   Pentamerus Beds here overlie Precambrian strata (see Itinerary 7A, localities 1 & 10). A diverse brachiopod fauna characterises these rocks and interbedded silty shales contain conodonts and acritarchs.

9. THE WREKIN & THE ERCALL (SJ630082 outcrops and track sections)
   Precambrian volcanics of Uriconian age overlain unconformably by Cambrian Wrekin

Quartzite.

The Wrekin ridge provides the best and most varied exposures of Uriconian rocks in England (see Itinerary 8, localities 2,4,5,6,& 8). The Uriconian has provided important evidence in attempts to reconstruct the early evolution of an ancient sea called the Iapetus Ocean and provides a valuable link with other exposures in the early basement rocks of England, Wales and Canada. The Wrekin Quartzite (locality 3) contains a variety of sedimentary features which are a record of the submergence of the old Precambrian landmass by the sea in Cambrian times. The overlying greenish sandstones (locality 9) contain beds burrowed by marine animals and yield the oldest fossils in this region. These include brachiopods, hyolithellids and various, as yet, unclassified phosphatic forms.

10. CLEE HILL QUARRIES (SO594761 various quarries)
Clee Hills Sill intruded into Carboniferous Coal Measures.

The quarries (see Itinerary 9, Dhustone quarry) show the Clee Hills Sill emplaced into unconsolidated Coal Measures sediments. Exposures provide fresh nepheline normative olivine-dolerites. The quarries are important in illustrating the relationship between alkaline magmatism, tectonics and sedimentation in the later stages of the Carboniferous Period in the Midlands.

11. CORNBROOK DINGLE (SO602757-603755 steep stream section)
Cornbrook Sandstone Formation of Namurian age.

This SSSI is the type section for the Cornbrook Sandstone (see Itinerary 9). It shows the nature of the sediments deposited on the St. George's Land during Namurian Times.

(list compiled by Martin Allbutt from data supplied by Andrew Herle of English Nature)

REGIONALLY IMPORTANT GEOLOGICAL (& GEOMORPHOLOGICAL) SITES (RIGS)

The RIGS concept is intended to supplement SSSI's in two respects:

(i) to designate sites of regional importance (which may also be of national importance)

(ii) to extend the criteria for designation beyond the purely "scientific" so as to include educational, aesthetic and historical values.

Designation is the responsibility of the local county based RIGS Group which, in Shropshire, comprises a small number of local geological enthusiasts. In its early years this voluntary Group was apt to concentrate on the "sites" aspect designating a relatively large number of small single sites, typically old quarries with just a single unit of stratigraphy.

Of late, with growing confidence, the Group has chosen to more fully exploit the inherent flexibility of the RIGS concept and give priority to larger but self-contained areas containing multiple stratigraphic units and geomorphological features. Where possible these areas have, by virtue of sympathetic ownership or management, guaranteed public access. RIGS designation will now imply a continuing exercise of survey and documentation. With adequate funding proposals for public presentation (trails, leaflets, guides, interpretation boards etc.) will be made, such as the "Shaping of Shropshire" programme.

With continuing designation and re-designation any list of RIGS will soon become out of date. However, for the record and as an indication of progress the following are designated RIGS relevant to itinerary localities within this guide:

RIGS NAME	ITINERARY	LOCALITY(S)
ASHES HOLLOW	1	1 to 9
STIPERSTONES	4	3a & 3b
SNAILBEACH MINE	4	SO373022
BERGAM QUARRY	4	5a
TASKER QUARRY	4	SO324956
HOPE VALLEY	4	SJ342015
GOGGIN ROAD	5	1 to 4
DEER PARK ROAD	5	5 to 8
SUNNYHILL TRACK	5	9 to 11
IPPIKINS ROCK	6	SO568965
EATON TRACK	6	1a to 1c
DELBURY QUARRY	6	11
HILLEND	7A	1
RIDGEWAY QUARRY	7A	9
BURY DITCHES (DAWES LINES)	7B	3 to 5
BURY DITCHES (WITHINS WOOD)	7B	6 to 8
LAWRENCE HILL QUARRY	8	1
WREKIN HILL	8	2 to 8
MADDOCK'S HILL QUARRY	8	12
TITTERSTONE CLEE (DHUSTONE)	9	SO596778
CORNBROOK DINGLE	9	SO602757
BIDGNORTH CASTLE HILL GDNS.	10	3
HIGH ROCK	10	7
WORFE BRIDGE	10	9

(list compiled by Martin Allbutt from information supplied by Shropshire RIGS Group, Oct. 2001)